# Contents

Introduction

The Abacus model

The Abacus materials are designed and written to allow for a daily, structured mathematics lesson:

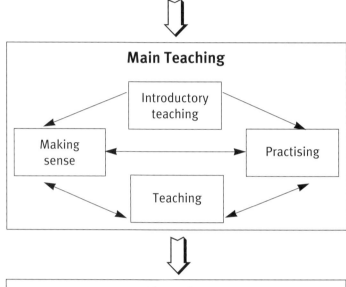

Mental Warm-up Activities
- Rehearsing previously-taught strategies
- Counting
- Number facts

Main Teaching

Introductory teaching

Making sense

Practising

Teaching

Plenaries
- Reinforcing key skills
- Addressing common difficulties
- Concluding with feedback or an activity

Each day's teaching begins with a whole class mental maths activity. These are presented in the **Mental Warm-up Activities** book.

The main part of the lesson is supported by the **Teacher Cards**:

- the front of each card gives support for whole class teaching for the first day of a topic
- the back of each card gives advice on further teaching for subsequent days and references to the practical activities included in this book. References to relevant **Textbook** pages and **Photocopy Masters** are also provided.

Each lesson is rounded-off with a plenary session. Guidance on key points to reiterate, common misconceptions to look out for, and whole class activities is included on the back of each Teacher Card.

Activity Book

The activities in this book are intended as follow-up to the introductory teaching. Each unit of the programme is supported by a range of activities covering different styles, numbers of children, resources etc.

Each activity includes the following information:

- Appropriate number of children, e.g. pairs, 3-4 children, whole class.

- A list of relevant materials. Any 'specialist' resources, e.g. number grids, number tracks ... are provided as Photocopy Masters at the back of the book. Number lines, number cards, place-value cards etc. are supplied separately in the **Resource Bank**.

- Level of difficulty, indicated by the following codes:

  basic work

  for all children

  enrichment and extension.

- Learning points are also provided, drawing on the teaching objectives from the Teacher Card. These learning points will assist the teacher in directing the group and making informal assessments. They are also useful as key points to highlight in the plenary session – it may be beneficial to give the children some points to consider when setting up the activity. This will give them a clear focus for the outcome of the activity and any key points they might raise in the plenary session.

- A number of ICT activities are included (these assume some prior knowledge of relevant software, e.g. spreadsheets).

Whole class work

Following the initial teaching input, it is often a useful strategy to carry out some immediate consolidation, with the whole class or large group, working on an appropriate activity. Many of the units include a whole class activity specifically written to support this strategy. Such activities are indicated by the icon:

We suggest that following the initial teaching input for the whole class activity, the children are arranged in pairs or small groups, and work independently for a short period exploring or consolidating their learning. These activities will sometimes lead into the plenary session, where the topic can be rounded-off with a discussion about what the children have learned and any difficulties they encountered.

Classroom management

When working with groups it is important to have a manageable number of groups (about four is ideal). It may be appropriate for one or two of those groups to be working from a Textbook or Photocopy Master page. You may decide to have more than one group working on the same activity concurrently. You should try to focus your attention on one or two groups, working intensively with them, directing, discussing, evaluating etc. The Abacus model assists management by ensuring that all the children are broadly working within the same topic, at the same time as providing differentiated work through the activities in this book and the Photocopy Masters.

The activities are written with enough detail covering resources and learning outcomes (as well as the description of the activities themselves) to allow any support staff to easily manage groups you are not working with directly.

ACTIVITY 1
Whole class, in pairs

- *Recognising the value of each digit in a 3-digit number*
- *Recognising 1/10/100 more/less than a 3-digit number*

Number cards (0 to 9) (PCM 1), place-value board (H, T, U) (PCM 13) per pair

Discuss the place-value boards and practise using them, with the children, making 2- and 3-digit numbers. Say a number, e.g. *Four hundred and sixty-one.* The children create the number on their place-value board with their cards, i.e. 461. Repeat several times, with variations, e.g. after hearing the number the children have to create the number which is 1 more; 1 less; 10 more; 10 less; 100 more or 100 less.

 ACTIVITY 2
3-4 children

- *Reading a 3-digit number*
- *Writing a 3-digit number when hearing it*

Place-value cards (hundreds, tens and units) (PCMs 10 to 12)

Shuffle the cards separately and place them face down in three piles. The children take turns to pick one card from each pile to make a 3-digit number, which they hide from the others. The child says the number, e.g. *Three hundred and forty-nine.* The other children write down the number, i.e. '349'. The first child reveals her cards so that the others can check their written number against it. Repeat several times.

 ACTIVITY 3
3-4 children

- *Recognising the value of each digit in a 3-digit number*

Two sets of place-value cards (hundreds, tens and units) (PCMs 10 to 12), Base Ten equipment (hundreds, tens and units)

Shuffle the cards separately and place them face down in three piles. One child takes a card from each pile and makes a 3-digit number, which he hides from the others. The child reads the number aloud, e.g. *Four hundred and fifty-three,* and the other children match it using Base Ten equipment, i.e. four hundreds, five tens and three units. They write the number and compare it with the cards. If the numbers match, they place the equipment and the cards together. Continue with the children taking turns to draw the cards until they have matched ten numbers.

 ACTIVITY 4
3-4 children

- *Recognising the value of each digit in a 3-digit number*
- *Recognising the largest of several 3-digit numbers*

Place-value cards (hundreds, tens and units) (PCMs 10 to 12), coins (£1, 10p, 1p), counters

Shuffle the cards separately and place them face down in three piles. Each child takes a card from each pile and creates a 3-digit number, e.g. 251. The children match their numbers with coins, i.e. two £1 coins, five 10p coins and one 1p coin, checking each other's calculation. The child with the most money wins that round and takes a counter. Replace the money and cards. Continue until one child has five counters.

 ACTIVITY 5
3 children

- *Writing 3-digit numbers in sequence in ascending order and descending order*

A one-minute timer

One child chooses a 3-digit starting number, e.g. 345, sets the timer and says, *Go!* The other two children each write the starting number, and underneath it as many numbers as they can in ascending order, i.e. '345, 346, 347, ...'. They stop after one minute. Look at the lists. How many mistakes are there? Are the numbers written correctly? Are there any missing? The children repeat the activity, taking different roles, and sometimes writing the numbers in descending order.

N2 Place-value

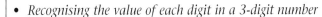

ACTIVITY 1
Whole class, in pairs

- *Recognising the value of each digit in a 3-digit number*
- *Beginning to compare and order 3-digit numbers*

Number cards (0 to 9) (PCM 1), place-value board (H, T, U) (PCM 13)

Select three cards at random, e.g. 3, 5 and 8. Ask the children to select the same three cards and to make different 3-digit numbers according to your instructions. E.g. *Make: the largest number* (853); *the smallest number* (358); *the smallest odd number* (583); *a number with five in the tens place* (358 or 853); *a number more than 600* (853 or 835), and so on. Discuss the correct number after each activity. Change the three cards and repeat several times.

ACTIVITY 2
2 pairs

- *Partitioning a 3-digit number into hundreds, tens and units*
- *Reading and writing a 3-digit number*

Place-value cards (hundreds, tens and units) (PCMs 10 to 12)

Shuffle the cards separately and place them face down in three piles. One pair takes one card from each pile, and makes a 3-digit number, unseen by the other pair. They read the number, e.g. *Two hundred and fifty-eight.* The other pair writes the number in hundreds, tens and units, i.e. '200 + 50 + 8'. Ask the first pair to spread out the three place-value cards to check. Repeat several times with the children taking different roles.

ACTIVITY 3
3 children

- *Recognising the value of each digit in a 3-digit number*

Place-value cards (hundreds, tens and units) (PCMs 10 to 12), a blank dice with 'H', 'T' and 'U' on each of two sides, cubes

Shuffle the cards separately and place them face down in three piles. Take one card from each pile to make a 3-digit number, e.g. 356. Each child throws the dice and collects cubes to match the value of the digit thrown. For example, if it shows 'T', then the child collects cubes to match the tens digit, i.e. 5 cubes. Continue for several rounds, making different 3-digit numbers. Ask the children to group their cubes in tens. Who collects the most?

ACTIVITY 4
3-4 children

- *Recognising the value of each digit in a 3-digit number*
- *Partitioning a 3-digit number into hundreds, tens and units*

Two sets of number cards (0 to 9) (PCM 1), counters

Shuffle the cards and deal three to each child. Each child secretly arranges his cards to make a 3-digit number. Ask them to reveal their numbers. The child with the largest hundreds digit collects three counters, the child with the largest tens digit collects two counters and the child with the largest units digit collects one counter. In the event of any ties, no counters are collected. The children replace the cards and repeat for ten rounds. Who collects the most counters?

ACTIVITY 5
3-4 children

- *Writing a 3-digit number in words*

Number cards (0 to 9) (PCM 1)

Shuffle the cards and deal three to each child to create a 3-digit number, e.g. 562. Each child writes the number, i.e. 'five hundred and sixty-two'. They check each other's spelling and count the number of letters needed to write the number, i.e. 22. Repeat for different numbers. Which numbers use many letters? Which use few?

ACTIVITY 1
Whole class, in pairs

• *Adding pairs which total 20*
Number cards (0 to 20) (PCMs 1, 2), petal cards (PCM 14) or scrap paper per pair
The children write five numbers between 0 and 20 on their petals. Shuffle the number cards and place them in a pile face down. Take a card. Show the children. Ask them the addition pair to make 20. E.g. card 5, you write 15 on the board, '5 + 15 = 20'. Any pair with 15 written down can cross it out. Turn over another card and repeat. Continue until one pair has crossed out all of their numbers.

ACTIVITY 2
3 children

 • *Adding pairs which total 20*
Number cards (0 to 20) (PCMs 1, 2), interlocking cubes
The children work together to find pairs of cards that make 20. How many pairs can they find? They write them all down and take one cube for each pair. Extend the activity by using two sets of cards. How many sets of three cards can the children find that make 20, e.g. 13 + 5 + 2?

ACTIVITY 3
3-4 children

• *Adding pairs which total 20*
Number cards (0 to 20) (PCMs 1, 2), number grid 1 (PCM 15)
Shuffle the cards and place them face down in a pile. The children take turns to remove a card and place it on the number on the grid which pairs with it to make 20. If the card has no corresponding number, the child keeps it. The children continue until all the grid numbers are covered. Who has the most cards left? The child with the highest total on their remaining cards wins.

ACTIVITY 4
2-3 children

 • *Adding numbers which total 20*
Number cards (0 to 20) (PCMs 1, 2), blank 3 × 3 grid (PCM 16)
Working together the children place the 10 card in the centre of the grid. They try to place eight other cards on the grid so that every row and every column adds up to 20. Check their grids. If they are correct, they can repeat with a different number at the centre.

11	7	2
4	10	6
5	3	12

ACTIVITY 5
3 children

 • *Adding pairs which total 10*
Two sets of number cards (0 to 10) (PCMs 1, 2), interlocking cubes
Place one set of cards in order, 0 to 10, in a line to make a number track. Shuffle the second set of cards and place them in a pile face down. The children take turns to reveal a card. Each child places his card on top of the number on the track which pairs to make 10, e.g. 3 on top of 7. The other children must agree that this is correct. If it is, the child takes a cube. Repeat until all the cards have been placed on the track.

ACTIVITY 6
Pair

 • *Adding pairs of numbers to make 20*
Spreadsheet software
The teacher prepares a spreadsheet file similar to the one shown. Column A – the teacher enters numerals up to 20. Column B – contains a plus sign. Column C – the children enter the addition pair to make 20 (the children will know if their answer is correct if the cell in Column D changes to 20). Column D – the teacher enters the formula '= A1 + C1 ...'

	A	B	C	D
1	14	+	6	20
2	15	+		15
3	11	+		11
4	9	+		9

ACTIVITY 7
3-4 children

• *Adding pairs of numbers to make 10*
Game 1: 'Butterfly bonds', two dice, counters (10 per child)
(See instructions on the card.)

N4 Addition

ACTIVITY 1
Whole class, in pairs

- *Making amounts using the fewest coins (up to 30p)*

Price labels (PCM 23), coins (1p, 2p, 5p, 10p, 20p) (one set per pair)

Give out one price label to each pair. The children decide how they will make up the amount on their label using the fewest possible coins. Give them five minutes to do this. Check together. Repeat with each pair receiving a new price label.

ACTIVITY 2
3-4 children

- *Adding three or four numbers (looking for pairs to make ten)*

Number cards (10 to 20) (PCMs 1, 2), three dice, interlocking cubes

Shuffle the cards and place them face down in a pile. The children take turns to throw the three dice and turn over a card. They add all four numbers and score as follows: find a number to make 10, take one cube; add the numbers correctly, take four cubes. The children check each other's additions and scoring. When all the cards have been used, who has the most cubes?

ACTIVITY 3
3 children

- *Adding three numbers (looking for pairs to make ten or 20)*

Number cards (0 to 20) (PCMs 1, 2), post-it notes

Divide the cards into 0 to 10 and 11 to 20. Shuffle each set and place them in two piles face down. Each child takes a card from either pile. They turn over their cards and together find the total, deciding on the best way of adding the three numbers together. They write the total on a post-it note, put the three cards together and place the post-it note on top. Repeat until all the cards have been used. Are all the totals correct?

ACTIVITY 4
3-4 children

- *Adding three numbers (looking for pairs to make 20)*

Number cards (1 to 20) (PCMs 1, 2)

Working together, the children draw a rough triangle. They write a multiple of 3 in the middle. They then write a number in each corner of their shape so that the numbers in each corner add up to the number in the middle. The numbers in the corners must be consecutive, e.g. a triangle with 15 in the middle must have 4, 5, and

6 written in the corners. How many triangles can they draw like this? Extend to drawing pentagons using a multiple of 5 in the middle.

ACTIVITY 5
3 children

- *Adding three numbers (looking for pairs to make ten)*

Two sets of number cards (0 to 10) (PCM 1), post-it notes

Shuffle the cards and place them in a pile face down. The children take turns to reveal a card. Each child places his card face up. One child guesses at the total of the three cards added together. The children then work together to find out the correct total. They write the total on a post-it note and put all the cards with it. If the guess was correct, that child keeps the pile. Repeat until all the cards have been used.

ACTIVITY 6
2-3 children

- *Addition pairs to 20*

Game 2: 'Three to win', number cards (1 to 20) (PCMs 1, 2), cubes
(See instructions on the card.)

ACTIVITY 1
Whole class, in pairs

• *Adding a 1-digit to a 2-digit number without crossing the tens*
Small number grid (0 to 99) per pair (PCM 35), coins (10p), a counter per pair
Each pair puts their counter on any number on the grid, except a multiple of ten. Write a number between 1 and 7 on the board, e.g. '4'. The children have to try to move their counter four spaces without needing to change row, i.e. they can only move their counter if it is on a number ending in 6 or less (27 forward four would result in moving down a row). Write another number on the board, e.g. 2. The children move again, if they can. If a pair lands on a multiple of ten, they take a 10p coin and place their counter on a new number anywhere on the grid. Continue, choosing new starting numbers until one pair has 50p.

ACTIVITY 2
3-4 children

• *Adding a 1-digit to a 2-digit number*
Two dice, interlocking cubes
Each child throws the two dice to create a 2-digit number and writes it down. Then, one child throws one dice. All the children look at the number thrown and work out the total if it is added to the number they have written down. If it will be more than the next multiple of 10, they take a cube. If not, they write the addition. They repeat the activity and after six turns, the winner is the child with the fewest cubes.

ACTIVITY 3
3-4 children

• *Recognising the number needed to make the next ten*
Number cards (1 to 100) (PCMs 1 to 7), interlocking cubes
Shuffle the cards and place them face down in a pile. The children take turns to remove a card, e.g. 54 and say what number needs to be added to reach the next ten, i.e. add 6, to make 60. The others check. If correct, the child collects a matching number of cubes, i.e. six. The winner is the first to collect 50 cubes (they should stack them in tens).

ACTIVITY 4
3 children

• *Recognising addition pairs to 20*
Coins (20p, 10p, 1p), post-it notes
Each child takes a handful of 1p coins and one 10p coin. They count up their total and write it on a post-it note. The first child reads out her amount. The other two decide how much more she needs to make 20p, select the correct number of 1p coins and give them to the first child. She checks by counting on to see if she has one 10p and ten 1p coins. If correct, she writes the whole addition on her post-it, e.g. '14p + 6p = 20p' and then swaps the ten 1p coins for a 10p coin. If incorrect, the children work together to correct the amount. Repeat for each child.

ACTIVITY 5
Pair

• *Adding to the next hundred*
Number grid 2 (PCM 17), blank 5×5 grid (PCM 18), counters
One child puts a counter on a number on the grid. The other child decides what number should be added to make the next hundred. They discuss the answer and if they agree, they write it into the matching space on the blank grid. They continue until the blank grid is complete.

ACTIVITY 6
3-4 children

• *Adding 9 to a 2-digit number*
Game 3: 'Fishy nines', dice, counters, cubes, calculator
(See instructions on the card.)

N6 Subtraction

ACTIVITY 1
Whole class, in pairs

• *Subtracting a 1-digit from 2-digit number to leave a multiple of ten*
A dice, counters
The children work in pairs. Each pair writes three numbers between 20 and 80 on a piece of paper (none should be multiples of ten). Throw a dice and write the number on the board, e.g. 4. The children subtract that number from their written numbers, in their heads. If any of the subtractions will give an answer that is a multiple of ten, they tell you their answer. If they are correct, they take a counter. Throw the dice again and keep playing. When you have thrown the dice several times, who has the most counters?

ACTIVITY 2
3-4 children

• *Subtracting a 1-digit from a 2-digit number, using addition bonds as a strategy*
Number cards (10 to 50) (PCMs 1 to 4), coins (10p, 1p), a dice, post-it notes
Shuffle the cards and place them face down in a pile. The children take turns to reveal a card, then match it with coins. One child throws the dice. They all look at their amounts and decide if they can give away a matching number of 1p coins, without breaking into a 10p coin. If they can, they write the matching subtraction on a post-it, stick it on their card and place it face up on the table in front of them. If they can't, the card is discarded. They each take another card and repeat six times. Who has fewest cards in front of them?

ACTIVITY 3
3-4 children

• *Recognising that if we subtract a 1-digit from a 2-digit number, with the same units digit, it leaves a multiple of ten*
Number cards (1 to 100) (PCMs 1 to 7), interlocking cubes
Shuffle the cards and place them face down in a pile. The children take turns to reveal a card, e.g. 54 and say what number must be subtracted to leave the 'last ten', i.e. take away 4 leaves 50. The others check they are correct and the child receives the matching number of cubes, i.e. four cubes. They continue until one child has collected 30 cubes.

ACTIVITY 4
3 children

• *Subtracting to leave a multiple of ten*
Number cards (10 to 50) (PCMs 1 to 4), coins (1p, 10p), post-it notes
Shuffle the cards and place them face down in a pile. The children take turns to reveal a card. They look at their card and decide what number they need to subtract to leave a multiple of ten. Each child writes her guess on a post-it note. They each look at their card again, match the number with coins, then check how many 1ps they can take away to leave only 10p coins. Together, they check the number on their post-it note. If correct, they take a cube. Continue until one child has ten cubes.

ACTIVITY 5
3-4 children

• *Subtracting a 1-digit from a 2-digit number*
Number cards (1 to 10) (PCM 1), coins (10p, 5p)
Shuffle the cards and place them face down in a pile. Each child begins with a score of 100. The children take turns to reveal a card and subtract it from their score. They replace the card at the bottom of the pile. They continue until a child reaches 0. If a child's score at any stage reaches a multiple of ten, they collect 10p. Who has collected the most money?

N7 # Numbers to 1000

ACTIVITY 1
Whole class, in pairs

- *Counting in ones or tens from a 3-digit number*
A dice, 10p coins, paper
Each pair chooses a starter 3-digit number, using the digits 1 to 6 (no pair should have the same starting number.) They write it down at the top of their paper. Say *Go!* One child from each pair writes down 3-digit numbers, counting up in ones from their starting number. After two or three minutes, say *Stop!* Throw a dice three times and write the numbers thrown on the board, e.g. '4, 6, 2'. Each pair must use these numbers to try to create a 3-digit number which matches any number on their list i.e. '246'. If any pair succeeds they collect 10p. Repeat, swapping roles until one pair has 20p.

ACTIVITY 2
3-4 children

- *Counting in ones or tens from a 3-digit number*
An egg timer, counters
One child acts as the time keeper. The children all agree a starting number. The time keeper says *Go!*, turns over the egg timer and, as fast as they can, the others write down numbers, counting in tens from the starting 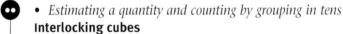 number, e.g. 326, the children write '326, 336, 346...' They continue until the egg timer runs out and the time keeper says *Stop!* Without looking at the papers, the time keeper guesses the last number that the children have written. The children compare their final numbers and the time keeper's guess. Any child whose last number matches the guess takes a counter. Together they check their lists, then repeat with a different child being the time keeper.

ACTIVITY 3
3-4 children

- *Estimating a quantity and counting by grouping in tens*
Interlocking cubes
Each child takes two large handfuls of cubes. They combine their cubes and estimate how many cubes there are. Each child writes down their estimate. Together they count the cubes, taking it in turns to count ten. They count the groups of ten and any loose cubes and say how many there are. By how much did each estimate differ from the actual total? Each child, in turn, must count out loud from the smaller number to the larger number to find out. They write the actual number below their guess and then write the difference. Repeat several times.

ACTIVITY 4
3-4 children

- *Counting in ones from 100*
An egg timer, post-it notes
The children take turns to count in ones, starting at 100 and returning to 100 when they reach 1000. They turn over the egg timer and count around the group. When the egg timer runs out, each child writes down on a post-it note the last number he said. They check each other's numbers (they should be consecutive). Then they restart the egg timer and repeat the procedure. Vary the activity by starting at 200 or 300, ...

ACTIVITY 5
Pairs

- *Estimating a quantity and checking an estimate*
Picture books
The children estimate the number of words in the book. They take turns to look at the pages and then each writes down an estimate. They decide how to check their estimates, compare the actual number with their estimates, then repeat with another book.

N8 Numbers to 1000

ACTIVITY 1
Whole class, in pairs

- *Saying the number ten more or ten less than any 3-digit number*
A dice, £1 coins
Each pair chooses a 3-digit starter number and writes it down. Throw the dice three times, e.g. 3, 1, 6. Write all the possible 3-digit numbers on the board, '361, 316, 136, 163, 631, 613'. Say the numbers and point at each of them in turn. Ask the children for the number ten more and ten less in each case. Repeat for the number which is 100 more and 100 less in each case. If any pair has any of these numbers written down, they receive a £1 coin. That pair writes a new number. Repeat several times.

ACTIVITY 2
3 children

- *Counting in hundreds from a 3-digit number*
Place-value cards (hundreds, tens, units) (PCMs 10 to 12), interlocking cubes
Shuffle the place-value cards separately and place them in three piles, face down. Each child takes one card from one of the piles to create a 3-digit number. The first child writes the number which is 100 more than this number. He passes the paper to the second child who writes the number which is 100 more than that. He then passes the paper to the third child who does the same. Continue until someone has to write a number over 1000. That child takes a cube. Repeat the activity. When all the cards have gone, who has the most cubes?

ACTIVITY 3
3-4 children

- *Adding ten to a 3-digit number (or recognising the number which is ten less)*
Place-value cards (hundreds, tens, units) (PCMs 10 to 12), interlocking cubes
Shuffle the cards separately and place them in three piles face down. The children take turns to remove a card from each pile, e.g. 200, 50, and 4, to create a 3-digit number each, which they write down, i.e. 254. They check each other's numbers, then each child writes the number ten less and ten more than her number. Again they check each other's and collect a cube for each correct answer. Continue until each child has collected ten cubes.

ACTIVITY 4
3-4 children

- *Counting in tens*
Blank 5×5 grid (PCM 18)
The children write a 3-digit number in the centre of the grid. They work together to decide the numbers which belong in the other spaces on the grid, according to these criteria: the number above is ten less; the number below is ten more; the number to the left is one less, and the number to the right is one more. Continue on the same basis to complete the grid.

ACTIVITY 5
3 children

- *Recognising numbers which have a difference of ten or one hundred*
Place-value cards (hundreds, tens, units) (PCMs 10 to 12), interlocking cubes
Shuffle the cards separately and place them in three piles face down. Each child writes down four 3-digit numbers. They then each take three cards, one from each pile, and create a 3-digit number. They lay out all three numbers in the middle. If any of them has a number on their paper which is ten or one hundred more or less than one of the numbers they have created, they take a cube. (If they have the same number they take two cubes.) Continue until all the cards have been used. Who has the most cubes?

N9 Multiplication/division

ACTIVITY 1
Whole class, in pairs

- *Understanding multiplication as repeated addition*
- *Multiplying two numbers (less than 6) together*

Two dice, interlocking cubes (36 per pair)

Roll two dice. The children make towers of cubes, according to the dice. E.g. a 3 and a 4, they make three towers of four cubes. They count how many cubes are needed, i.e. 12, then record the multiplication, i.e. '3 × 4 = 12'. Give them a couple of minutes then ask them to hold up their answers. Repeat for 10 throws of the two dice.

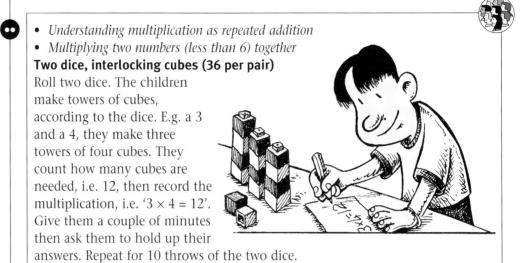

ACTIVITY 2
2-3 children

- *Understanding multiplication as repeated addition*
- *Multiplying by 2/3 by counting in twos/threes*

Coins (1p)

The children make several piles of two 1p coins. They use these to write some ×2 multiplications, e.g. '2 × 2, 3 × 2, 4 × 2'. Ask them to do the same with piles of three 1p coins.

ACTIVITY 3
3-4 children

- *Multiplying two numbers together*

Multiplication cards (PCMs 25 to 27), counters

Shuffle the cards and place them in a pile, face down. One card is revealed, e.g. 2 × 5, and the children make two sets of five counters. They count how many counters are needed, and the first child writes the multiplication, i.e. '2 × 5 = 10'. Continue turning over the cards and taking turns to record the complete multiplications until each child has written six multiplications.

ACTIVITY 4
3-4 children

- *Multiplying two numbers together*
- *Dividing by linking division to multiplication*

Multiplication cards (PCMs 25 to 27), interlocking cubes

Shuffle the cards and place them in a pile, face down. Each child is dealt one card, e.g. 3 × 4, and must make a matching multiplication with the cubes, i.e. three towers of four. They use these towers to write a matching multiplication and a matching division, i.e. '3 × 4 = 12, 12 ÷ 4 = 3'. They check each other's towers and their multiplications and divisions. They replace the cubes and repeat the activity several times.

ACTIVITY 5
3-4 children

- *Multiplying two numbers (less than 9) together*
- *Using an array*
- *Dividing by linking division to multiplication*

Number cards (0 to 9) (PCM 1), squared paper

Shuffle the cards and deal out two of them, e.g. 3 and 7. The children each draw a 3 by 7 rectangle on the squared paper, to show three rows of seven squares. They count the number of squares inside the rectangle to obtain a multiplication, and record it. They use their rectangle to record a corresponding division.

N10 Multiplication/division

ACTIVITY 1
Whole class, in pairs

- *Multiplying by 2*
Number cards (1 to 10) (PCM 1), coins (10 × 2p) per pair
Shuffle the cards and place them face down in a pile. The children take turns to remove a card, e.g. 7, and say the matching number of twos, i.e. *Seven twos are fourteen*. Their partner checks by laying out seven 2p coins, counting in twos, *Two, four, … fourteen*. If correct, the first child keeps the card. Repeat several times.

ACTIVITY 2
2-3 children

- *Recognising and reciting the 'twos' in sequence*
Number cards (1 to 20) (PCMs 1, 2)
The children lay out the cards in two rows of ten, in order, so that 1 is above 2, 3 is above 4, ... They look along the second row at the multiples of two and say them together. They then practise saying them without looking.

ACTIVITY 3
3-4 children

- *Recalling ×2 multiplication facts*
Multiplication cards (×2) (PCM 25), interlocking cubes, counters
Shuffle the cards and place them in a pile face down. The children take turns to reveal a card, say and then write the complete multiplication. They can use towers of two cubes to check. If correct, they take a counter. If they can correctly say and write a matching division they take another counter. They check each other's answers. When all the cards have been used, reshuffle and start again. Who is the first to collect ten counters?

ACTIVITY 4
3-4 children

- *Recalling ÷2 division facts*
- *Linking division to multiplication*
Division cards (÷2) (PCM 29), interlocking cubes, 2p coins
Shuffle the cards and place them in a pile face down. The children take turns to reveal a card and say the answer to the division. They can use towers of two cubes to check. If correct, they take coins to match the answer, e.g. if the answer is 6, they take three 2p coins. They check each other's answers. When all the cards have been used, reshuffle and start again. Who is the first to collect 30p?

ACTIVITY 5
3-4 children

- *Finding the ×2 multiplication fact which matches a given answer*
- *Linking division to multiplication*
Multiplication cards (×2) (PCM 25), even cards (2 to 20) (PCMs 1, 2), counters
Shuffle the multiplication cards and spread them out face up. Shuffle the even cards and place them in a pile face down. The children take turns to reveal a number card and find the matching multiplication card for which the number card is the answer. They check each other's answers. If correct, they take a counter. When all the cards have been used, reshuffle and continue.

ACTIVITY 6
2-3 children

- *Recognising the pattern of the multiples of two on a number grid*
2 cm squared paper
The children write the numbers 1 to 4, in order, in a row, then '5, 6, 7, 8' on the row below, and so on up to 40. They colour the 'twos' squares. Repeat for grids with different numbers of columns. Discuss the patterns created.

ACTIVITY 7
pairs

- *Recalling ×2 multiplication facts*
Spreadsheet software
The teacher prepares a spreadsheet file similar to the one shown. Column D – the children enter the answer to the multiplication (and check the cell in Column E says 'Correct'). Column E – the teacher should have previously used the 'If logical' function, =IF(D1=A1*C1;"Correct";"Try again") …

	A	B	C	D	E
1	2	×	1	2	Correct
2	2	×	2		
3	2	×	3		

ACTIVITY 1
Whole class, in pairs

• *Doubling a number (1 to 10)*
Two sets of number cards (1 to 10) (PCM 1), interlocking cubes (per pair)
Shuffle the cards and place them face down in a pile. The children take turns to reveal a card, e.g. 7, and say double the number. Each pair makes two towers of seven cubes to check. If correct, the child keeps the card. If not, it is returned to the bottom of the pile. Continue until all the cards have been collected.

ACTIVITY 2
2-3 children

• *Recognising the doubles of numbers (1 to 10)*
Number cards (1 to 10) (PCM 1), number cards (2, 4, 6, ... 20) (PCMs 1, 2), interlocking cubes
The children lay out the cards (1 to 10) in a line and place a matching tower of cubes on the top of each card. They make another set of the same towers to show the double of each number and place these on the corresponding cards. They place the even number cards (2, 4, 6, ...) in position below to show each double. Finally, they put the cubes away and turn the 'doubles' cards face down and try to say the doubles. They can reveal the cards to check.

ACTIVITY 3
2 pairs

• *Halving a number (2 to 20)*
Number cards (2, 4, 6, ... 20) (PCMs 1, 2), interlocking cubes, counters
Shuffle the cards and place them in a pile, face down. Each pair takes turns to reveal a card, e.g. 16, and says half the number. To check, they can collect a matching number of cubes and build two equal towers. If they are correct and haven't used any cubes, they collect two counters. If the cubes are needed, they collect one counter. When all the cards have been revealed, reshuffle them and continue. Which pair collects the most counters?

ACTIVITY 4
3 children

• *Doubling a number (1 to 12)*
Number cards (4, 6, ... 24) (PCMs 1 to 3), counters (three colours), two dice (1 to 6)
The children place the cards in a line, in order, to make a track. They take turns to throw both dice, find the total and double it. They place a counter on the matching number card. The winner is the first to have three of her counters on one card.

ACTIVITY 5
2-3 children

• *Doubling a number (1 to 12)*
• *Halving a number*
Two dice (1 to 6), interlocking cubes (loose and in towers of ten)
The children take turns to throw two dice. If the total is odd, they double it. If the total is even, they halve it. They collect a number of cubes to match the answer. After five rounds, the winner is the child with the most cubes. Return the cubes and repeat. (Extend by using the two dice to create a 2-digit number.)

ACTIVITY 6
3-4 children

• *Doubling a number (1 to 10)*
Two sets of number cards (1 to 10) (PCM 1), two sets of number cards (2, 4, 6, ... 20) (PCMs 1, 2)
Children act out the function of a doubling machine. One child is handed a card (1 to 10). She passes through the 'machine' (carpet square or play house), picks up the correct 'double' (from the number cards 2, 4, 6, ...) and passes out of the 'machine'. The others check she is correct. They repeat taking turns.

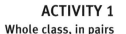

N12 Fractions

ACTIVITY 1
Whole class, in pairs

• *Recognising fractions of amounts*
Paper squares and circles, counters
Each pair takes a paper square (a cake) and divides it into four equal parts. They place one counter (a cherry) on each quarter, and write the matching fraction, i.e. $\frac{1}{4}$ of 4 = 1'. They then add another cherry to each part, and write $\frac{1}{4}$ of 8 = 2'. They continue adding equal numbers of cherries and writing the corresponding fractions of the amounts. Let them divide other 'cakes' into thirds or eighths and repeat the process.

ACTIVITY 2
2-3 children

• *Recognising simple fractions of shapes*
Paper squares, rectangles, circles (several of each, different sizes)
The children each choose a shape. They fold it in half, colour the halves differently, and write $\frac{1}{2}$ on each half. They choose another shape, fold it in quarters, colour the quarters differently, and write $\frac{1}{4}$ on each quarter. They repeat for a third shape, folding, colouring and labelling eighths.

ACTIVITY 3
2-3 children

• *Recognising simple fractions of shapes*
Fraction cards 1 (PCM 31)
Spread out both sets of cards, face down, in two separate areas. The children take turns to reveal one from each set. If they match ($\frac{1}{2}$ and a shaded half), they keep them and have another turn. If they don't match, they are turned back over and the next child has a turn. Continue until all cards have been removed. Who has collected the most? Reshuffle the cards and play again. Can they make more cards for each set?

ACTIVITY 4
2-4 children

• *Finding unit fractions of amounts*
Fraction cards 1 (top two rows of PCM 31), even cards (4, 6, 8, ... 20), (PCMs 1, 2), counters, score sheet
The cards are shuffled separately and placed face down in two piles. The children take turns to reveal one card from each pile, e.g. $\frac{1}{4}$ and 12 and decide the fraction of the amount, i.e. *One quarter of twelve is three.* They check each other's answers using the counters. If correct, they score a point. If a child reveals a fraction with a remainder, e.g. $\frac{1}{3}$ of 16, and can say the remainder, i.e. *One,* she scores another point. The children continue taking turns, reshuffling the cards if necessary. Who is the first to collect eight points?

ACTIVITY 5
2 pairs

• *Finding unit fractions of amounts*
• *Recognising remainders when finding fractions of amounts*
Fraction cards 1 (top two rows of PCM 31), coins (10p, 1p), counters
One pair takes a handful of coins and counts the total, e.g. 21p. The other pair takes a fraction card, e.g. $\frac{1}{3}$ and tries to divide the coins according to the fraction. If they can they write the division, i.e. $\frac{1}{3}$ of 21 = 7', they collect a counter. The children continue, sharing roles.

ACTIVITY 6
2-3 children

• *Recognising simple fractions on grids*
Fraction cards 1 (top two rows of PCM 31), blank 4×6 grids (PCM 20) (several copies), crayons or felt-tipped pens (one colour per child)
Shuffle the cards and place them face down in a pile. The children have two grids each and take turns to reveal a card and colour in the matching fraction of one of the grids. Used cards are returned to the bottom of the pack. The winner is the first to complete both grids. Repeat adding two 'one sixth' cards.

ACTIVITY 1
Whole class, in pairs

• *Adding two multiples of five*
Fives cards (5, 10, 15, ... 100) (PCMs 8, 9), coins (5p)
Each child chooses a multiple of five beyond 50 and writes it down. Choose two cards and show the children. Write a matching addition on the board, e.g. '35 + 40 =' . Ask the children what the total is, i.e. 75. Any pair with the answer written down receives a 5p coin and writes a new number. Repeat until all the cards have been used. Who has collected the most money?

ACTIVITY 2
3 children

• *Subtracting multiples of five*
Fives cards (5, 10, 15, ... 100) (PCMs 8, 9)
Shuffle the cards and place them in a pile face down. Each child takes a card. Without showing the others, they add 25 to their card number and write down the answer. They take turns to pass the answer to the other two. Each child looks at the answer and works out the corresponding fives card, i.e. they must subtract 25. They write down what they think, below the original number. When each child has had a guess, they compare their answers with the card number. Who was correct? Repeat several times.

ACTIVITY 3
Pairs

• *Adding or subtracting ten or five from a multiple of five*
Coins (5p, 10p)
Each child takes some 10p coins and a 5p. They work out how much they have and write down the amount. They swap papers and work out how much their partner will have if either 10p or 5p is taken away (they decide on the amount). They then write down the answer. The partner then removes the appropriate coin from their piles, counts the money and writes down the amount left. Was it what they expected?

ACTIVITY 4
3-4 children

• *Adding or subtracting multiples of five*
Fives cards (5, 10, 15, ... 100) (PCMs 8, 9), coins (5p)
Spread out the cards face down. Each child writes down a multiple of ten, e.g. '30'. They take turns to turn over two cards. If the sum **or** difference is the multiple of ten chosen by that child, she collects a coin. The cards are turned back over. The children may not turn over the same cards twice. They play for two turns each, then start a new game, each choosing a new multiple of ten. After several rounds, discuss with them which multiple of ten 'answers' often occur and which do not.

ACTIVITY 5
Pair

• *Adding two multiples of five*
Spreadsheet software
The teacher prepares a spreadsheet file similar to the one shown. Column D – the children enter the answer to the addition (they will know that their answer is correct if the cell in Column E says 'well done'). Column E – the teacher should have previously used the 'If logical' function, =IF(D1=A1+C1;"Well done";"Try again") ... (The equals sign in Column D is a graphic.)

	A	B	C	D	E
1	15	+	55	=70	Well done
2	20	+	25	=	
3	5	+	10	=	

13

Addition

ACTIVITY 1
Whole class, in pairs

• Adding multiples of ten and five to make 100
**Fives cards (5, 10, 15 ... 100) (PCMs 8, 9),
petal cards (PCM 14) or scrap paper**
Each pair writes down five multiples of
five on their petal card. Take a fives
card and show it to the children. They
have to decide the number which goes
with it to make 100. If any pair has
that number written down, they may
cross it out. Continue playing until one
pair has crossed out all of their
numbers. Repeat several times.

ACTIVITY 2
3 children

• Adding multiples of ten and five to make 100
Fives cards (5, 10, 15 ... 100) (PCMs 8, 9)
Spread out the cards face down on the table. The children take turns to reveal
two cards. If the cards add up to 100, they keep them. If not, they turn them
back over. Continue playing until all the cards have gone. Who has most pairs?

ACTIVITY 3
3-4 children

• Adding multiples of ten and five to make 100
Coins (5p, 10p, £1)
One child takes some 10p coins and a 5p. She works out how much she has and
writes down the amount. The other children work out how much is needed to
make £1. They write down the amount. They then add that amount of money
to the original amount to see if it makes £1. If correct they each receive a £1
coin. If not, they check again. All the children write the matching addition.
Repeat several times with the children taking different roles.

ACTIVITY 4
3 children

• Adding multiples of ten to make 100
Number grid (1 to 100) (PCM 34), a dice, coins (10p)
The children take turns to throw the dice. One child takes that number of coins
and decides how much he has by placing a coin on each multiple of ten on
their grid, starting with 10. The others then work out how much more they
need to have £1 (ten 10p coins). They work this out by counting down the grid,
pointing to each multiple of ten without a 10p on it. When they agree how
much more is needed, they write the matching addition, e.g. '40p + 60p =
100p'. Repeat several times.

ACTIVITY 5
Pairs

• Adding multiples of ten and five to make 100
Blank 5 × 5 cross grids (PCM 21)
The children work together to complete number crosses
where the number in the middle is 100 and the column
and the row contain numbers which add to 100. However,
the crosses must be symmetrical, both horizontally and
vertically. How many crosses can they complete where the
numbers used are all multiples of five?

		25		
		25		
45	5	100	5	45
		25		
		25		

ACTIVITY 6
2 pairs

• Adding lengths in multiples of 5 cm to make 100 cm
String/thread, one metre rule, scissors
Each pair cuts a piece of string an exact multiple of 5 cm. The pairs swap string,
measure the length and cut another piece to make a total length of one metre.
They check each other's and then repeat for different lengths.

ACTIVITY 1
Whole class, in pairs

- *Recognising the value of each digit in a 3-digit number*
- *Ordering 3-digit numbers*
- *Recognising the largest and smallest of two numbers*

Number cards (0 to 9) (PCM 1), place-value board (H, T, U) (PCM 13) per pair

Select a card from your set of number cards. The children find the matching number card and place it in one of the three positions on their board. Select a second card, and ask the children to place this in one of the two remaining positions. Finally, do the same with a third number. Remind the children that once a card is in place it cannot be moved. The children read out their number and the pairs with the largest 3-digit number collect a counter. Replace all the cards and repeat several times. Who collects the most counters?

ACTIVITY 2
Pairs

- *Ordering 3-digit numbers*

Number cards (0 to 9) (PCM 1)

The children make three 3-digit numbers using all except one of their cards, e.g. 246, 379, 850. They then place them in order from the largest to the smallest and try to read each one aloud. They shuffle all the cards, make three new numbers and repeat the activity several times. The children can write each set of three numbers in order.

ACTIVITY 3
3-4 children

- *Recognising the value of each digit in a 3-digit number*
- *Ordering 3-digit numbers*

Place-value cards (hundreds, tens and units) (PCMs 10 to 12)

Shuffle the cards separately and place them face down in three piles. Each child takes a card from each pile, e.g. 300, 40 and 2, and makes a 3-digit number, i.e. 342, reading it aloud. The children place their numbers in order, from largest to smallest. They repeat until all the cards are taken and all **nine** 3-digit numbers are in order.

ACTIVITY 4
3-4 children

- *Ordering 3-digit numbers*
- *Creating 3-digit numbers from a given set of three digits*

Number cards (0 to 9) (PCM 1), counters

The children select any three cards, e.g. 5, 7 and 1. They arrange them to make a 3-digit number, e.g. 571. They rearrange them to make another, e.g. 715. They continue to investigate how many different 3-digit numbers they can make, and write them down. Finally, when they have found all the possible numbers, they write them in order from smallest to largest. Repeat for a different set of three cards. Is the amount of possible numbers the same?

ACTIVITY 5
2-3 children

- *Ordering 3-digit numbers*
- *Creating different 3-digit numbers given one fixed digit*

Number cards (0 to 9) (PCM 1), place-value board (H, T, U) (PCM 13)

The children place card 4 in the hundreds column. Using each of the other cards once only, how many different numbers can they make? They write them in order. Next, they place the 4 in the tens column, and again using each of the other cards once only, they make as many different numbers as they can. Finally, they do the same with the 4 in the units column. They then write all the different numbers, in order, from largest to smallest.

N16 Addition

ACTIVITY 1
Whole class, in pairs

- *Adding to the next ten and one more*

A large dice (1 to 6), petal cards (PCM 14) or scrap paper

Each pair writes down five 2-digit numbers ending in 1 on their petal card. Throw the dice twice. Create a 2-digit number and write it on the board, e.g. '24'. Now write the addition which takes that number to the next ten plus one, i.e. '24 + 7 ='. The children work out the total. If any pair has the matching number written down, they cross it out. Continue playing until one pair has crossed out all of their numbers.

ACTIVITY 2
4 children

- *Adding to the next ten*

Number cards (20 to 80 excluding the multiples of ten) (PCMs 2 to 6), counters

Shuffle the cards and spread them out face down. The children take turns to reveal a card. The child says the number that must be added to the card to make the next ten, e.g. card 43, the child says *And seven makes fifty.* If the others agree, he takes a matching number of counters. They all write down the matching addition. Repeat until one child has 30 counters.

ACTIVITY 3
3-4 children

- *Adding to the next ten*

Coins (1p, 10p)

Each child takes turns to collect some 10p and 1p coins. They work out how much they have and write down the amount. The others decide how much money they must add to reach the next multiple of ten. They write down the amount. The children check by adding the appropriate coins. If they are wrong, they should check again. Finally, they write down the addition. Repeat several times.

ACTIVITY 4
3 children

- *Adding to the next ten and beyond*

Place-value cards (tens and units) (PCMs 10 to 12), counters, post-it notes

Shuffle the cards separately and place them in two piles face down. The children, in turns, take a card from each pile to create a 2-digit number. They add 8 to their number and write the total. The other children check the answer. If it is correct, that child takes the same number of cubes as the number of units in their answer. E.g. a child takes a 30 and a 7, and makes 37. He adds 8 and gets a total of 45. He takes five cubes. Repeat several times, each time adding 8.

ACTIVITY 5
Pairs

- *Adding to the next ten and beyond*

Number cards (1 to 10) (PCM 1), two dice

One child throws the two dice and creates a 2-digit number. She writes down the number. The second child takes a card. He adds this number to the 2-digit number and writes the total. The first child takes a card and repeats the process adding her card to the new total. They continue like this (working through the cards several times if necessary) until the total goes over 100. Then they start again, creating a new 2-digit number. How fast can they reach 100 or beyond each time?

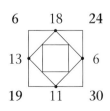

ACTIVITY 1
Whole class, in pairs

- *Finding the difference between two 2-digit numbers that are close together*

Number cards (1 to 10) (PCM 1) one set per pair, place-value cards (tens and units 1 to 5) (PCMs 10, 12), interlocking cubes

Shuffle the tens and units cards separately and put them in two piles face down. Each pair selects a number card, holding it so that everyone can see. Take one tens card and one units card and create a 2-digit number, e.g. 42. The children read aloud the number. Write another number, slightly smaller, on the board, e.g. '38'. The children work out the difference between these two numbers. If their chosen number matches the difference, they collect a cube. Continue.

ACTIVITY 2
4 children

- *Finding a difference (less than ten) between two 2-digit numbers*

Place-value cards (tens) (PCM 12), counters, post-it notes

Shuffle the cards and spread them out face down. The first child turns over a card. The second child writes a number which is slightly more than this number, and the third child writes a number which is slightly less than the number, e.g. card 40; the second child writes '45' and the third writes '37'. The fourth child works out the difference between the numbers. Together, they check. If correct, she takes that number of counters. They write the matching subtraction on a post-it note and stick it on the card. Repeat with the children taking different roles. When all the cards have been used, who has the most counters?

ACTIVITY 3
3-4 children

- *Subtracting the tens from a 2-digit number*
- *Recognising that the units digit represents the number left*

Coins (1p, 10p), post-it notes

One child takes some 1p and 10p coins. He works out how much he has and writes down the amount. The others write down how much will be left if the 10p coins are taken away. The first child removes the 10p coins and checks how much he has left. He then writes the matching subtraction on a post-it note, e.g. '45p – 40p = 5p'. Repeat several times with the children swapping roles.

ACTIVITY 4
2 pairs

- *Finding the difference between two numbers*

Two sets of place-value cards (tens and units) (PCMs 10 to 12), cubes, post-it notes

Shuffle the cards separately and place them in two piles face down. Each pair takes one card from each pile to create a 2-digit number. Each pair works separately to calculate the difference between the two numbers. They compare their answers. If they agree that they are correct, they each take a cube. If their answers differ, they work together to find out who is correct, and that pair takes a cube. They all write the matching subtraction on a post-it note and stick it on the cards. Repeat several times until one pair has ten cubes.

ACTIVITY 5
Pairs

- *Finding the difference between numbers*

Each pair draws a large square and writes a number in each corner. They work out the difference between each pair of numbers and write it in the middle of the line. They join these middle points, creating another square inside the first. They continue, repeating the process until the final square has 0 at each corner. Repeat with another large square.

```
  6        18        24


13                      6


 19        11        30
```

 **Money**

ACTIVITY 1
Whole class in pairs

- *Making amounts up to £10*
- *Adding and subtracting 10p coins*

Coins (1p, 10p, £1)
Each pair chooses an amount between £1 and £10 and writes it down. Take some £1, 10p and 1p coins and create an amount of money, e.g. £2.42. Show the children the coins and together work out the amount. Write it on the board. If a pair can match it with the amount they have written down by adding or subtracting either £1 or 10p coins, they may show you how. E.g. if a pair has written £2.12, they can subtract 30p from the amount on the board to equal their amount. Repeat several times.

ACTIVITY 2
4 children

- *Making amounts up to £2*
- *Adding and subtracting 10p coins*
- *Adding to £2*

Place-value cards (tens and units) (PCMs 10 to 12), coins (1p, 10p, £1), a dice
Shuffle the cards separately and place them face down in two piles. Each child takes a card from both piles and matches the amount with money, e.g. 30 and 5, they take 35p. They each take a £1 coin and write down their total amounts, i.e. £1.35. Each child throws the dice and collects that number of coins (they may choose to take 10p or 1p coins or a mixture). The object is to collect an amount as close as possible to £2. They each work out their new total and write a matching addition. They check each other's. Who is closest to £2? Play again until all the place-value cards have been used.

ACTIVITY 3
3 children

- *Subtracting 10p coins from an amount over £1*

Coins (1p, 10p, £1), post-it notes, interlocking cubes
One child takes a handful of mixed coins. The others work together to see how much she has taken and write down the amount. The first child removes one 10p and says the amount left. A second child does the same, and then the third child and so on. If there are only £1 and 1p coins, the children must exchange a £1 coin for ten 10p coins. They continue until there are only 1p coins left. The child who takes the last 10p coin wins and takes a cube. Repeat several times with the children swapping roles.

ACTIVITY 4
3 children

- *Making an amount of money using £1, 10p and 1p coins*

Place-value cards (hundreds, tens and units) (PCMs 10 to 12), post-it notes, coins (£1, 10p, 1p)
Shuffle the cards separately and place them in three piles face down. Each child takes a card from a pile to create one 3-digit number. They read their number. The child who took the units card matches the card with that number of 1p coins. The child who took the tens card matches that number with the appropriate number of 10p coins and the child who took the hundreds card does the same with the £1 coins. They look at their pile of coins and work out how much they have. They write the amount on a post-it note and stick it on their place-value cards. Repeat until they have used up all the cards.

ACTIVITY 5
2 pairs

- *Adding or subtracting 10p coins*

Coins (1p, 10p, £1), a dice, interlocking cubes
Each pair takes an amount of money, adds it up and writes down the total. Together they throw the dice, add that number of 10p coins to their total and write down the new amount. Each pair checks the other's addition. Whose amount is closest to an exact number of pounds? That pair takes a cube. Repeat.

ACTIVITY 1
Whole class, in pairs

- *Adding and subtracting two 2-digit numbers*

Coins (1p, 10p, £1), interlocking cubes

Each pair writes down an amount between 20p and 80p. Say an amount, e.g. *24p,* and write it on the board. The children add this to their amount and write down the total. Say a new amount, e.g. *31p.* The children subtract this from their total, and write down the new total. Repeat this several times. If at any stage, any pair has a total which is a multiple of ten, they shout out *Penguin* (or another chosen word) and the game starts again.

ACTIVITY 2
3 children

- *Adding and subtracting two 2-digit numbers*

Place-value cards (tens and units) (PCMs 10 to 12), number grid (1 to 100) (PCM 34)

Shuffle the cards separately and place them face down in two piles. One child takes a card from each pile and makes a 2-digit number. Another child finds the number on the grid. The third child takes another card from each pile and creates another 2-digit number. The children work together to add the two numbers together and write the addition. Then they work together to find the difference between the original two numbers and write the subtraction. Repeat the activity with the children taking different roles.

ACTIVITY 3
3 children

- *Finding the difference between two amounts of money*

Coins (1p, 10p), post-it notes

One child takes some 10p and some 1p coins, at least five of each. She writes the amount on a post-it note. Another child takes some coins, but this time less than five of each. After she has counted them and written the amount on the post-it note, the children compare the amounts and work out the difference. They write the matching subtraction. They repeat the activity, swapping roles, until they have at least six correct subtractions.

ACTIVITY 4
3 children

- *Adding a near multiple of ten*

Place-value cards (tens excluding 90, and units) (PCMs 10 to 12), number grid (1 to 100) (PCM 34), post-it notes

Shuffle the cards separately and place them in two piles face down. One child takes two cards and creates a 2-digit number. He reads the number, finds it on the grid and adds 21 to it. The children write the total on a post-it note and stick it on the cards. Repeat until all the cards have been used, changing roles.

ACTIVITY 5
Pairs

- *Adding or subtracting amounts of money*

Number cards (3 to 9) (PCM 1), coins (50p, 20p, 10p, 5p, 2p, 1p)

One child deals two cards. The children create a 2-digit number and write it down. They have to think of three amounts of money which, when added together, will equal that number. However, none of the three amounts can be a multiple of ten, and all of them must be more than ten. When they find three amounts, they write them down as an addition. Repeat several times. (As an extension, the children can match each addition using the fewest coins for each amount.)

N20 Addition/subtraction

ACTIVITY 1
Whole class, in pairs

- *Adding and subtracting near multiples of tens*

Number grid (1 to 100) (PCM 34) per pair, a dice, coins (10p), counters

Each pair chooses five numbers on the grid between 0 and 95 and places a counter on each. Throw the dice twice to create a 2-digit number and write it on the board, e.g. '35'. Choose a near multiple of ten, e.g. 29. The children choose to add or subtract this amount from the number on the board, e.g. 35 + 29 = 54 or 35 – 29 = 6. If the answer is a number hidden by one of their counters, they take 10p. Repeat several times. How long does it take someone to collect 20p?

ACTIVITY 2
3-4 children

- *Adding and subtracting a near multiple of ten to a 2-digit number*

Place-value cards (tens and units) (PCMs 10 to 12), number grid (1 to 100) (PCM 34), different coloured counters, coins (10p)

Shuffle the cards separately and place them face down in two piles. Each child takes a card from both piles and makes a 2-digit number. The children each find their numbers on the grid and place a counter on it. They work together to see if any two numbers are separated by a difference of 9, 19, 29, 39, 49, etc. If they are, they all take a 10p and write the matching subtraction. E.g. one child has a counter on 15 and another has a counter on 64, so they write '64 – 49 = 15'. They cross out the numbers used and repeat the activity.

ACTIVITY 3
3-4 children

- *Adding a near multiple of ten to a 2-digit number*

Number grid (1 to 100) (PCM 34), a dice, strips of paper, cubes

One child throws the dice. They write down the number at the top of a strip of paper. Another child chooses to add 19 or 29. He writes the total below the first number and passes the strip to the next child. She then adds 19 or 29 and writes the total below that and passes the strip to the next child. They continue until one of them has to write a number above 200. He takes a cube and the round stops. Repeat several times. Who ends up with the most cubes?

ACTIVITY 4
3 children

- *Adding nine by adding ten and taking away one*

Place-value cards (tens and units) (PCMs 10 to 12), number grid (1 to 100) (PCM 34), interlocking cubes, post-it notes

Shuffle the cards separately and place them in two piles face down. The first child takes two cards and creates a 2-digit number. The second child reads the number and finds it on the grid. The third child adds 9 to it. They all check. If correct, that child takes a cube, the children write the total on a post-it note and stick it on the cards. Repeat with the children changing roles until all the cards have been used.

ACTIVITY 5
Pairs

- *Subtracting near multiples of ten*

Starting with a total of 501, the children have to subtract ten 2-digit numbers (from 19, 29, 39 ... 99) and end up with 1. Each pair must find a different way of doing this.

Counting

ACTIVITY 1
Whole class

- *Counting and recognising multiples of 50*
Starting at 0, count in tens around the class, each child saying one number. Continue at a fairly quick pace. If a child says a multiple of 50, he comes and stands at the front. If he doesn't realise it is a multiple of 50, the next child says the number and comes to the front. Continue until you reach 1000. How many children are at the front? How many multiples of 50 are there between 1 and 1000? Repeat the activity, starting at 800 and counting to 1300.

ACTIVITY 2
3-4 children

- *Counting in hundreds*
A one-minute sand timer, interlocking cubes
The children agree a starting number, e.g. 324. Their aim is to count in hundreds around the group for one minute. Before they start, they each guess what number they will say as the timer runs out and write down their guess. They start the timer and begin counting, one number each in turn, *Three hundred and twenty-four, four hundred and twenty-four, ...* What number is said as the timer runs out? Compare this with the numbers they have guessed. The child with the closest guess takes a cube. Repeat several times with different starting numbers.

ACTIVITY 3
3-4 children

- *Recognising multiples of 50*
A dice (0, 1, 2, 3, 4, 5), interlocking cubes
Each child takes a turn to throw the dice three times. They write down the numbers thrown and create their own 3-digit number. Anyone who can make a number which is a multiple of 50 takes five cubes. Anyone who can make a number which is a multiple of 5 takes one cube. Repeat several times. Who ends up with the most cubes?

ACTIVITY 4
3 children

- *Recognising multiples of 100*
PCM 36 (second strip) or long strips of paper (marked with at least 21 spaces) felt-tipped pens
On the strip of paper, write 100 at the first mark and 110 at the second. Each child then takes turns to fill in the next mark, counting in tens. They continue, checking each other's numbers until they have filled in all the marks on the strip. They count along the strip and decide which numbers are multiples of 100 and circle those in red. Then they take another strip, start numbering at 500, and repeat the process.

ACTIVITY 5
Pairs

- *Recognising multiples of 10, 50 and 100*
- *Organising information and investigating in a systematic fashion*
The children calculate the number of: multiples of 100 between 0 and 1000, multiples of 50 between 0 and 1000, and multiples of 10 between 0 and 1000. Can they use this information to decide how many multiples of 100, 50 and 10 there are between 0 and 10000?

N22 Odd and even

ACTIVITY 1
Whole class, in pairs

- *Recognising even and odd numbers*
Dice, paper (headed 'odd' or 'even') per pair
Divide the class so that one half is collecting odd numbers and the other half even numbers. Give each pair a piece of paper headed 'even' or 'odd'. Throw the dice twice and write the numbers on the board, e.g. '5' and '2'. Together, arrange the digits to make two 2-digit numbers. E.g. 52 and 25. They write four numbers (either odd or even) on their paper between those two numbers. Check the answers together. Repeat several times.

ACTIVITY 2
3 children

- *Counting in twos*
- *Recognising even and odd numbers*
Number grid (1 to 100) (PCM 34), coins (2p), counters
One child chooses a starting number on the grid and places a counter on it. The second child says whether the number is even or odd. The third child starts at 2 and counts in twos, taking 2p for each number spoken. She continues until she reaches or passes the number with a counter on it. Did she say the counter number? If she did, the number is even and can be made using 2p coins. If not, the number is odd. Was the second child right? If so, he keeps the counter. Play at least 12 times with the children swapping roles. Who has the most counters?

ACTIVITY 3
3 children

- *Recognising even and odd numbers*
A dice, coins (1p, 2p), post-it notes
One child throws the dice twice. The second child writes down the numbers thrown and creates a 2-digit number. The third child makes that number using 2p coins. If she can make it exactly, the number is even. The other children check that she is correct. The first child has to share out the coins between the other two children. They may need to split the last 2p. How much have they got each? They write a matching addition on a post-it note, e.g. '17p + 17p = 34p'. If it is odd the first child keeps all the coins. Repeat several times with the children taking different roles.

ACTIVITY 4
3 children

- *Recognising even and odd numbers*
Strips of squared paper at least 20 squares long, scissors
Using the strips of paper, the children each decide how long to make their strip (between 2 and 20 squares). They cut it to the right length and write down the number of squares on a separate piece of paper. They look at each other's numbers and decide whether the numbers are even or odd. Looking at one number at a time, the children take turns to cut their own strip to make two equal parts. It cannot be cut across the middle of a square. If the strip will divide into two equal parts, then the number is even. They write 'even' next to the number. They continue until they have labelled each number even or odd. Repeat, choosing new numbers.

ACTIVITY 5
Pairs

- *Recognising even and odd numbers*
Coins (2p)
Each child has a bank of ten 2p coins. One child writes down a 3-digit number. He keeps it hidden from his partner who has to guess the number. He can only ask questions which relate to 'even' and 'odd'. E.g. *Is the hundreds/tens/units digit even or odd? Do the digits add together to make an even or an odd number?* When he has asked five questions, he can start guessing. He may ask more questions. Each guess costs 2p which he pays to his partner. When he has guessed the number, the children change roles and repeat the activity.

N23 **Addition/subtraction**

ACTIVITY 1
Whole class, in pairs

• *Adding pairs of multiples of five to make 100*
Fives cards (5, 10, 15 ... 100) (PCMs 8, 9), petal cards (PCM 14) or scrap paper
Each pair chooses five multiples of five between 5 and 100 and writes them down on their petal card. Shuffle the fives cards and place them in a pile face down. Take a card and read out the number. Subtract the number from 100. If any pair has the answer written down they cross it out. Continue until one pair has crossed out all five numbers. Repeat, starting with five new numbers.

ACTIVITY 2
3 children

• *Adding pairs of multiples of five to make 100*
Blank addition grids (PCM 22), number cards (1 to 9) (PCM 1), number grid (1 to 100) (PCM 34)
Shuffle the cards and place them in a pile face down. Each child takes an addition grid and takes turns to reveal a card. They write the card number in the first box and a five in the second. They then have to work out what number goes with that number to make 100. They write this number in the space opposite, so that the two numbers, read horizontally, add to make 100. They replace the card at the bottom of the pile and continue down the grid. They check each other's together.

ACTIVITY 3
3 children

• *Adding pairs of multiples of five to make 100*
£1 coins
One child writes down a multiple of five between 5 and 100 and hides it from the others. She says the number which goes with it to make 100. E.g. she writes 35 and says, *Sixty-five*. The other children listen, and guess the number that was secretly written down. If correct, the first child takes a £1 coin. Repeat with the children taking different roles. Who has the most money?

ACTIVITY 4
3 children

• *Adding multiples of ten to make 100*
Two sets of tens cards (0 to 100) (PCM 8)
Shuffle the cards and spread them out face down. The children take turns to turn over two cards. If they add up to 100, the child keeps the cards. If not, she turns them back over and another child has a go. When all the cards have gone, who has the most pairs?

ACTIVITY 5
Pairs

• *Adding numbers to make 100*
A dice
One child throws the dice twice and makes a 2-digit number. The other child looks at the dice and writes down the number which goes with it to make 100. Repeat several times with the children taking different roles. How many possible pairs can they find?

N24 **Addition**

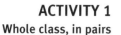

ACTIVITY 1
Whole class, in pairs

• *Doubling multiples of five*
Fives cards (5 to 100) (PCMs 8, 9), petal cards (PCM 14) or scrap paper
Each pair chooses five multiples of ten between 10 and 200 and writes them down on their petal card. Shuffle the fives cards and place them in a pile face down. Take a card and read out the number. The children double that number. If any pair has the answer written down they cross it out. Continue until one pair has crossed out all five numbers. Repeat, starting with five new numbers.

ACTIVITY 2
4 children

• *Doubling multiples of five and simple 2-digit numbers*
Blank addition grids (PCM 22)
One child takes a grid and writes down, in the first two boxes on the left hand side, a multiple of 5 which is less than 100 or a 2-digit number where the units and the tens digits are both less than 5, e.g. 34, 21, 43... She passes it to the child on her left. That child doubles the number written down and writes it in the opposite space. He then writes another number, according to the same criteria in the second two boxes on the left hand side and the grid is passed round again. The children continue until all the grid is complete. They then place the grid in the centre of the table and mark it, working together to ensure that all the doubles are correct. Repeat with new grids.

ACTIVITY 3
3 children

• *Doubling multiples of five and simple 2-digit numbers*
Coins (1p, 5p, 10p), counters
One child collects an amount of money under 50p, where the units digit is 5p or less. The second child collects the same amount. The third child has to write down the original amount and work out the double. The children then combine the two amounts and check to see if the third child has doubled it correctly. If she has, she takes a counter. Repeat several times with the children taking different roles.

ACTIVITY 4
3 children

• *Doubling simple 2-digit numbers less than 50*
Place-value cards (tens and units) (PCMs 10 to 12)
Spread out the cards face up on the table. One child writes down a number less than 50, where the units digit is less than 5. The second child creates that number using the appropriate place-value cards. The third child finds a tens card and a units card which are double the first ones. They put them together and check that this number is double the first number. If they agree, they write the double next to the original number and replace the cards. Repeat with the children taking different roles.

ACTIVITY 5
Pairs

• *Doubling 2-digit numbers*
One child writes down a number between 1 and 20. The other child doubles it and writes down the answer. The first child doubles that number and writes down the answer. They continue, creating a chain of doubles. However, they must stop doubling when they write a number containing an 8. How long a chain can they create?

11   22   44   88

ACTIVITY 1
Whole class, in pairs

- *Multiplying by 5*
Number cards (1 to 10) (PCM 1), coins (10 × 5p) per pair
Shuffle the cards and place them face down in a pile. The children take turns to reveal a card, e.g. 8, and say that number of fives, i.e. *Eight fives are forty.* The other child checks the answer by laying out eight 5p coins, counting in fives as she does so: *Five, ten, fifteen, twenty, ...* If she is correct, the first child keeps the card. The children continue until all the cards are revealed.

ACTIVITY 2
Pairs

- *Multiplying by 5*
Pegs, peg-board
One child makes one row of five pegs. The other child records the number of pegs: '1 × 5 = 5'. He then adds a second row of five pegs which the first child records: '2 × 5 = 10'. They continue, alternately arranging the pegs and recording the total, stopping at any time after 10 × 5.

ACTIVITY 3
3-4 children

- *Recalling ÷10 and ÷5 division facts*
Fives and tens cards (PCMs 8, 9), interlocking cubes (towers of 5 and 10), coins (5p, 10p)
Shuffle the cards and place them in a pile face down. The children take turns to reveal a card and say a division. They can use towers of five or ten cubes to check. If they are correct, they write the division and take the correct number of 5p or 10p coins, e.g. 30, they take three 10p coins or six 5p coins. They check each other's answers. When all the cards have been used, reshuffle and start again. Who is the first to collect £1.50?

ACTIVITY 4
Pairs

- *Recognising multiples of 5 and 10*
- *Recalling ×10/×5 multiplication facts*
Number grid (1 to 100) (PCM 34), 20 counters per child, a dice, 2 cubes
The children each place their cube on 1. They take turns to throw the dice and move their cube that number of spaces. Every time they land on a multiple of 5 they give their opponent one counter, and on landing on a multiple of 10, they give her two counters. They try to say the multiplication which matches the number they land on. The game finishes when one child reaches 100.

ACTIVITY 5
2-3 children

- *Recalling ×10/×5 multiplication facts*
- *Constructing division facts (÷5 and ÷10) linked to multiplication facts ×5, ×10*
Multiplication cards (×5 and/or ×10) (PCMs 26 to 28), counters
Shuffle the cards and spread them out, face down. One card is revealed and all the children write the resulting multiplication, e.g. '7 × 5 = 35', and also a matching division, i.e. '35 ÷ 5 = 7'. They check each other's answers. They collect one counter for each correct multiplication and division. When the cards have all been used, reshuffle and start again.

ACTIVITY 6
Pair

- *Recalling ×5 multiplication facts*
Spreadsheet software
The teacher prepares a spreadsheet file similar to the one shown. Column D – the children enter the answer to the multiplication (and look to see if the cell in Column E says 'Correct'). Column E – the teacher should have previously used the 'If logical' function, =IF(D1=A1*C1;"correct";"Try again") ... (The equals sign in Column D is a graphic.)

	A	B	C	D	E
1	5	×	1	= 5	Correct
2	5	×	2	=	
3	5	×	3	=	

Multiplication/division

ACTIVITY 1
Whole class, in pairs

- *Multiplying two numbers (up to 6) together*

Two dice (per pair), counters or cubes (36 per pair)

The children take turns to roll the two dice, e.g. 3 and 5, then multiply together the number of spots on each side. They check each other's multiplication by making rows of counters, i.e. three rows of five counters. They score one point for each correct multiplication. Who is the first player to collect ten points?

ACTIVITY 2
2-4 children

- *Understanding multiplication as describing an array*

Squared paper, scissors, glue

The children cut out rectangles from their squared paper, e.g. two squares by five squares. They mount the rectangles on a sheet of paper, and write the matching multiplications alongside, i.e. '2 × 5 = 10'. Repeat several times.

ACTIVITY 3
Whole class or group

- *Recalling multiplication facts up to 6 × 6*

Two dice, counters, interlocking cubes (in towers from 1 to 6), rectangles of card

Play a game of Bingo. Each child makes a Bingo card by drawing four circles on their card and writing a number from 1 to 36 in each circle. Roll the two dice and call out the numbers, e.g. *Three and two*. The children work out the answer, i.e. 3 × 2 = 6. Show three towers of two cubes to check the answer. Any child with a 6 on their card can cover it with a counter. The winner is the first child to cover all four numbers.

ACTIVITY 4
Pairs

- *Recalling multiplication facts up to 6 × 6*

Number grid 3 and grid window (PCM 19), counters

The children place the window on different parts of the number grid, either horizontally or vertically. They multiply the two outlined numbers together and record the answers. They can place the counters in rows to check the multiplications. They investigate all the different possible answers. Which is the largest number they can make and which is the smallest?

ACTIVITY 5
3-4 children

- *Understanding multiplication as describing an array*
- *Recalling multiplication facts up to 6 × 6*
- *Creating division facts linked to multiplication facts*

Multiplication cards (PCMs 25 to 28), pegs, peg-board

Spread the cards out, face down. The children take turns to reveal a card, e.g. 3 × 4, and say the answer to the multiplication, i.e. *Twelve*. Together, they can make three rows of four pegs on the pegboard to check. They then try to write a matching division, looking at the rows of pegs. They check each other's answers. If they are correct, the first child keeps the card. If not, the card is placed in the reject pile. Continue until all the cards have been revealed. Ask them to turn over all the rejected cards and try to say the multiplications and matching divisions, checking with the pegs if necessary.

ACTIVITY 6
2-3 children

- *Recalling multiplication facts up to 6 × 6 and beyond*
- *Creating division facts linked to multiplication facts*

Multiplication cards (PCMs 25 to 28), blank card

Shuffle the multiplication cards and spread them out, face down. The children take turns to reveal a card and say the answer to the multiplication, together with a matching division. They check each other's answers. If correct, they keep the card. Who collects the most? Make some new multiplication facts cards, e.g. 7 × 10, 6 × 6. Add these cards to the set, reshuffle the cards, and play again, several times. Add more cards when the children are confident.

ACTIVITY 1
Whole class, in pairs

- *Multiplying by 3*
Number cards (1 to 10) (PCM 1), ×3 multiplication table (for checking) (PCM 30)
Shuffle the cards and place them face down in a pile. The children reveal a card, e.g. 4, and say the number of threes, i.e. *Four threes are twelve*. They check by chanting the multiples of three using their fingers then the ×3 table. Repeat.

ACTIVITY 2
2-3 children

- *Creating the ×3 multiplication table*
2 cm squared paper
The children write the numbers '1, 2, 3' in three squares to form a row on the squared paper. They write '4, 5, 6' in the second row, and so on up to 30. They then write the ×3 multiplication table, writing '1 × 3 = 3' beside the first row, …

ACTIVITY 3
2-3 children

- *Multiplying by 3*
Blank 5×5 grid (PCM 18), number grid 3 (PCM 19), calculator
The children work together to multiply each grid number by 3, and record the answers in the matching spaces on the blank grid. They use a calculator to check.

ACTIVITY 4
3-4 children

- *Recalling the ×3 multiplication facts*
Multiplication cards (×3) (PCMs 25, 26), interlocking cubes (in towers of 3)
Shuffle the cards and place them in a pile, face down. The children take turns to reveal a card, say and then write the multiplication. They can use towers of three cubes to check. They check each other's answers. When all the cards have been used, reshuffle and start again.

ACTIVITY 5
2-3 children

- *Recalling the ×3 multiplication facts*
- *Linking ÷3 division facts to ×3 multiplication facts*
Multiplication cards (×3) (PCMs 25, 26), division cards (÷3) (PCM 28), interlocking cubes (in towers of 3)
Shuffle the multiplication cards and place them in a pile, face down. Spread out the division cards, face up. The children take turns to reveal a multiplication card and say the answer. They can use towers of three cubes to check. They then look for the matching division card. If they are correct they take both cards and place them in front of them, side by side. Finally, they place all the cards in order from the smallest answer to the largest, matching the multiplications with their divisions. Reshuffle the cards, and play again.

ACTIVITY 6
3-4 children

- *Recalling the ×3 multiplication facts*
Game 4: 'Space Race', dice, counters, cubes, a calculator
(See instructions on the card.)

ACTIVITY 7
2-3 children

- *Searching for patterns in the digits of the multiples of 3*
2 cm squared paper
The children write the multiples of 3, in order to 30. They find the digit sum of each multiple, e.g. for 12, 1 + 2 = 3; for 18, 1 + 8 = 9. They look for patterns in the answers. They represent the pattern on squared paper by drawing a line three units long, turning clockwise through one right angle and drawing a line whose length matches the next digit sum, i.e. 6. They continue turning through one right angle and drawing straight lines whose length matches the next digit sum.

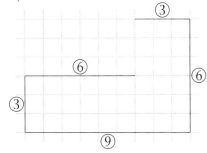

Fractions

ACTIVITY 1
Whole class, in pairs

- *Recognising fractions which are several parts of a whole*
- *Representing fractions with non-unit numerators*

Number cards (1 to 9) (PCM 1), squared paper
Draw a blank fraction on the board (as shown). Shuffle the cards and spread them out face down. Two children select a card and place the smaller number above the larger one to show a fraction. The children colour a shape on their squared paper to match the fraction. E.g. if the fraction is $\frac{3}{5}$, they colour three squares in a 1×5 grid. The children check each other's drawings. Repeat the activity several times, creating different fractions.

ACTIVITY 2
2+ children

- *Recognising fractions which are several parts of a whole*

2 cm squared paper
The children draw four 2×2 grids, then colour and label the grids to show quarters: $\frac{1}{4}, \frac{2}{4}, \frac{3}{4}$ and $\frac{4}{4}$. They then draw eight 2×4 grids and colour and label each to show eighths: $\frac{1}{8}, \frac{2}{8}, \dots \frac{8}{8}$.

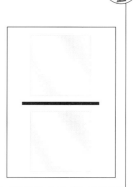

ACTIVITY 3
2-3 children

- *Recognising fractions which are several parts of a whole*

Fraction cards 1 to 3 (PCMs 31 to 33)
Spread out both sets of cards (fractions and shaded shapes), face up, in two separate areas. The children take turns to choose a matching pair, one from each set, and place them as a pair in front of them. Continue until all possible pairs have been removed. How many cards are left over? Reshuffle the cards and play again.

ACTIVITY 4
2-3 children

- *Representing fractions with non-unit numerators*

Fraction cards 3 (PCM 33), blank 4×6 grids (PCM 20 – several copies), crayons or felt-tipped pens
Shuffle the cards and place them face down in a pile. One card is revealed, e.g. $\frac{2}{3}$. One child colours the matching fraction of the first grid. The next card is revealed and a second child colours the matching fraction. They continue, moving on to new grids until all the cards have been revealed.

ACTIVITY 5
2-4 children

- *Finding fractions of amounts (with non-unit numerators)*

Fraction cards 3 (PCM 33), 24 interlocking cubes, counters
Shuffle the cards and place them in a pile, face down. The children take turns to reveal a card, e.g. $\frac{3}{4}$. They then say that fraction of 24, i.e. *Three quarters of twenty-four is eighteen.* They check each other's answers using the cubes. If they are correct, they collect a counter. Continue, reshuffling the cards if necessary. Who is the first to collect eight counters?

Place-value

ACTIVITY 1
Whole class, in pairs

- *Rounding a 3-digit number to its nearest 100*

Number cards (0 to 9) (PCM 1)

Select three cards to create a 3-digit number. Choose a pair to say its nearest 100. The other pairs check the answer. Rearrange the cards to make a different 3-digit number and choose another pair. When all possible 3-digit numbers have been made with the three cards, replace them with three different numbers and repeat.

ACTIVITY 2
2-3 children

- *Rounding a 2-digit number to its nearest 10*

Number cards (0 to 9) (PCM 1), 10-division number lines (PCM 36 – several copies), place-value board (PCM 13)

Label the ends of the number line '30' and '40'. The children place the 3 card in the tens column of the place-value board ready to make a 2-digit number. The other cards are shuffled and turned over one at a time to be placed in the units column alongside the 3, e.g. 37. They write 37 on the line and say its nearest ten, i.e. *Forty.* Continue through the thirties, then repeat, choosing a different tens card and a new number line.

ACTIVITY 3
3-4 children

- *Rounding a 3-digit number to its nearest 100*

Place-value cards (hundreds, tens, units) (PCMs 10 to 12), 100-division number lines (PCM 36 – several copies)

Label the ends of the number line '200' and '300'. The children select the 300 card, and the tens and units card are shuffled separately and placed face down in two piles. One child selects one tens card and one units card to create a 3-digit number between 300 and 400. Another child has to write it on the line, and a third child says its nearest hundred. The children then remove and discard the tens and units cards and repeat, changing roles. Continue like this until all the tens and units cards have been used. Repeat using a different hundreds card and a new number line.

ACTIVITY 4
2-4 children

- *Rounding a 3-digit number to its nearest 100*
- *Rounding a 3-digit number to its nearest 10*

Coins (£1, 10p, 1p), cloth bag

Place the coins in the bag. Each child takes a handful of coins, adds up how much they have taken and writes the amount, both to the nearest pound (100p) and to the nearest 10p. The children then pass on their money to the child on their left, who then writes this new amount of money to the nearest pound and nearest 10p. Continue like this until all the amounts of money have been round once. The children check the totals and nearest £1 and 10p agree. Replace all the money in the bag and repeat.

ACTIVITY 5
3 children

- *Rounding a 3-digit number to its nearest 100*

Number cards (0 to 9) (PCM 1), counters

Decide together on a multiple of 100, e.g. 600. Deal three cards each. Each player tries to make a 3-digit number whose nearest 100, is the chosen multiple of 100, e.g. 587 or 623. If successful they collect a counter. Repeat. The winner is the first to collect eight counters.

Addition/subtraction

ACTIVITY 1
Whole class, in pairs

• *Adding 2-digit numbers using multiples of 5*
Petal cards (PCM 14)
Each pair writes down five 2-digit multiples of 5 on their petals. Write '105' on the board. Can any pair use two, three or four of their numbers to make this total? Repeat several times with different numbers on the board.

ACTIVITY 2
4 children

• *Adding 2-digit numbers using multiples of 5*
Coins (5p)
The children each write down a 2-digit multiple of 5. One child adds up all four and writes down the total. The others decide if she is correct. If so, they award her 5p, and write out the addition. The children each choose a new multiple of 5 and another child adds them up. Repeat several times.

ACTIVITY 3
3 children

• *Adding 2-digit numbers using multiples of 5*
Blank 5×5 grid (PCM 18), counters or cubes
The children fill in the blanks on their grid with 2-digit multiples of 5. They put a counter over each number so they cannot be seen. They take turns to remove three counters and add the three numbers revealed. What is the total? The children work it out individually and then check their answers. Who is correct? They write out the correct addition. Repeat a few more times.

ACTIVITY 4
4 children

• *Adding 2-digit numbers using multiples of 5*
Coins (1p, 5p, 10p)
Each child takes some 10p and 5p coins. They each work out how much they have and write down the total. They choose a partner and work in pairs to find out how much they have altogether. They write the additions. The pairs then swap additions and check that they are correct. The children then return their coins and start again, taking a new amount each.

ACTIVITY 5
Pairs

• *Adding 2-digit multiples of 10*
The children work out how many different ways they can find of making exactly 100 by adding several multiples of 5. However, no two multiples can be the same. E.g. they can have 25 + 15 + 10 + 50, but not 25 + 25 + 15 + 35.

N31 Subtraction

ACTIVITY 1
Whole class, in pairs

- *Subtracting one 2-digit number from another without having to cross 10*
Two dice, petal cards (PCM 14) or scrap paper
Each pair writes down five 2-digit numbers on their petal card. Write '65' on the board. Throw the dice. Use the numbers thrown to create a 2-digit number and write it as part of a subtraction, e.g. '65 – 42 = '. Read the subtraction together. The children calculate the answer. If any pair has the answer written down, they cross it out. Repeat several times, occasionally changing the starting number, e.g. to 77, until one pair has crossed out all their numbers.

ACTIVITY 2
3 children

- *Subtracting multiples of ten from a 2-digit number*
Coins (1p, 10p)
One child takes some 10p and 1p coins. He adds them up and writes down the amount. The second child decides how many 10p coins to take away, and writes down that amount. The third child counts back to work out how much will be left when that amount is taken away. They all complete the written subtraction, then take away the second amount from the first and check that the calculation is correct. If correct, the third child keeps 10p. Repeat several times with the children taking different roles.

ACTIVITY 3
Pairs

- *Subtracting one 2-digit number from another using the strategy of counting back in tens*
Number grid (1 to 100) (PCM 34)
One child writes a number between 40 and 90, e.g. '57'. Her partner writes a number with smaller units and tens digits. The first child writes the appropriate subtraction, e.g. '57 – 32'. Her partner uses the number grid to help him work out the answer, counting back in tens initially. The first child writes in the answer. They repeat the process, taking different roles. Continue until they have written ten subtractions.

ACTIVITY 4
Pairs

- *Subtracting 2-digit numbers*
Number cards (2, 4, 6, 8, 9) (PCM 1)
The children choose four cards each time and arrange them to make two 2-digit numbers. They subtract one from the other and write the subtraction. Repeat ten times.

N32 Addition/subtraction

ACTIVITY 1
Whole class, in pairs

- *Finding the difference between two close numbers*
Number cards (20 to 100) (PCMs 2 to 7), petal cards (PCM 14) or scrap paper
Shuffle the number cards and place them in a pile face down. Each pair writes down five 1-digit numbers on their flower. Choose a child to take a card. He writes the number on the board, e.g. '68'. Write a subtraction using the number on the board, e.g. '73 – 68 ='. Read the subtraction together. The children calculate the answer. If any pair has that number written down, they cross it out. Continue until one pair has crossed out all of their numbers.

ACTIVITY 2
3 children

- *Finding the difference between two close numbers*
Coins (1p, 10p), number cards 1 to 5 (pile A) (PCM 1), number cards 5 to 10 (pile B) (PCM 1)
One child takes a card from pile B (and takes that many 10p coins) and a card from pile A (and takes that many 1p coins). She adds them up and writes down the amount. The second child takes one less 10p and a few more 1p coins. He writes down that amount. The third child works out the difference between the two amounts. They all complete the written subtraction and check that it is correct. Repeat several times with the children taking different roles.

ACTIVITY 3
4 children

- *Subtracting one 2-digit number from another by finding the difference*
Number cards (10 to 80) (PCMs 1 to 6), a dice
Spread out the cards face up on the table. One child throws the dice. The children look at the number thrown, e.g. 6. Using the cards, they try to find pairs of numbers whose difference is that number, e.g. 45 – 39, 22 – 16. How many can they find? They score one point for every pair of cards they can find. Repeat several times with different children throwing the dice.

ACTIVITY 4
4 children

- *Recognising what must be added to a 2-digit number to make the next ten*
Number grid (1 to 100) (PCM 34), counters (five each of four different colours)
The children choose counters of the same colour and take turns to place one on the grid. Each child says the number he places it on, e.g. *Forty-five*. That child then says how many to reach the next ten, i.e. *five*. The others check by counting on the grid. If the child is correct, he leaves his counter on the grid. If not, he removes the counter. The children continue until one of them has five counters in a row in any direction, including diagonally.

ACTIVITY 5
Pairs

- *Finding the difference between two 2-digit numbers*
- *Recognising patterns*
Place-value cards (tens and units) (PCMs 10 to 12)
The children use the cards to create pairs of 2-digit numbers, e.g. 45 and 53. How many pairs can they make with a difference of eight? Is it possible to use all the cards to make pairs with difference of eight? Extend the activity by asking them to make pairs with a difference of seven or six.

ACTIVITY 6
3-4 children

- *Finding the difference between two 2-digit numbers*
Game 5: 'Dinosaur difference', 30 cubes, calculator
(See instructions on the card.)

Addition

ACTIVITY 1
Whole class, in pairs

- *Adding three numbers using the strategy of adding multiples of five*
Fives cards (5 to 50) (PCMs 8, 9), two dice
Shuffle the cards and place them in a pile face down. The children each write down a number between 60 and 100. Choose two children to take a card each. Show the class the numbers e.g. 35 and 15. Throw the dice to create another 2-digit number, e.g. 34. Each pair writes down the three numbers and adds them up. Agree the total and write it on the board. They then work out the difference between the number they first wrote down and the total on the board. The pair with the smallest difference wins. Repeat several times.

ACTIVITY 2
3 children

- *Adding three numbers where two are multiples of five*
Coins (1p, 5p, 10p)
One child takes some 10p and 1p coins. He adds them up and writes down the amount. The other two children each take some 10p coins and a 5p coin. They also write down the amount they have. All the children work together to calculate how much they have in total. When they have agreed on the total, they combine their coins, exchange the two 5p coins for a 10p, and add up the total amount. Was their calculation correct? Repeat several times, with the children taking different roles.

ACTIVITY 3
3 children

- *Adding three numbers where two are multiples of five*
Fives cards (5 to 100) (PCMs 8, 9), a dice, post-it notes
Spread out the cards face down on the table. One child throws the dice twice and creates a 2-digit number. He writes it on a post-it note. The other two children each turn over a card. Working on their own, they add up the three numbers, then compare answers. Are they the same? If not, they should work it out together. They write the answer on the bottom of the post-it note, and stick the note on the two cards. Repeat with the children taking different roles.

ACTIVITY 4
3 children

- *Adding two multiples of five*
Fives cards (5 to 100) (PCMs 8, 9), coins (5p, 10p)
Shuffle the cards and place them in a pile face down. The children each take a card. They match the amount on their card with coins, using 10p coins and one 5p if necessary. They then have to add the three amounts and work out the total. If possible, they exchange two 5p coins for a 10p coin. Finally, they each write the corresponding addition. Repeat several times.

ACTIVITY 5
Pairs

- *Adding multiples of five*
- *Adding 2-digit numbers*
How many additions can be created where consecutive multiples of five are added to total 100? E.g. 25 + 30 + 35 = 90 (… nearly: there is only one way – 10 + 15 + 20 + 25 + 30). Extend the activity by adding consecutive multiples of five which total 150 (30 + 35 + 40 + 45). Finally, try finding consecutive numbers (not necessarily multiples of five) to total 100 (18 + 19 + 20 + 21 + 22).

N34 Addition

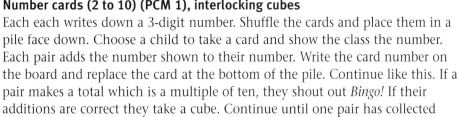

ACTIVITY 1
Whole class, in pairs

- *Adding 1-digit numbers to 3-digit numbers*
Number cards (2 to 10) (PCM 1), interlocking cubes
Each each writes down a 3-digit number. Shuffle the cards and place them in a pile face down. Choose a child to take a card and show the class the number. Each pair adds the number shown to their number. Write the card number on the board and replace the card at the bottom of the pile. Continue like this. If a pair makes a total which is a multiple of ten, they shout out *Bingo!* If their additions are correct they take a cube. Continue until one pair has collected three cubes. (You may wish to hand out 3-digit numbers with low unit values.)

ACTIVITY 2
3 children

- *Adding a 1- or 2-digit number to a 3-digit number*
Coins (1p, 10p), a dice, counters
The children each throw the dice and use the three numbers thrown to create a 3-digit number. They write down the number, e.g. '334'. Each child then takes a handful of coins (no more than four 10p or 1p coins), works out how much and writes it down, e.g. a child takes three 10p and four 1p coins and writes down 34p. Each child then adds that number to their original 3-digit number. They check each other's calculations. If they are correct, they collect a counter. Repeat several times.

ACTIVITY 3
4 children

- *Adding a 2-digit number to a 3-digit number*
Place-value cards (hundreds, tens and units) (PCMs 10 to 12), a dice, post-it notes
Spread out the cards face down in three separate piles. One child throws the dice twice and creates a 2-digit number. He writes this on the top of a post-it note. The other children each turn over a card from a different pile to create a 3-digit number. Working on their own, they add the two numbers, write down their answer and then compare answers. Are they the same? If not, they work it out together. They write the total on the bottom of the post-it note, and stick it on the three cards. Repeat several times with the children taking different roles.

ACTIVITY 4
3 children ●

- *Adding to make the next ten with 3-digit numbers*
Number cards (1 to 9) (PCM 1), place-value cards (hundreds, tens and units) (PCMs 10 to 12)
Shuffle the place-value cards separately and place them in three piles face down. Lay out the number cards in a line face up along the top of the table. The children each take a place-value card from a different pile and create a 3-digit number. They read the number together and decide how many there are to the next ten, e.g. they have the number 356 and have to decide how many to 360. They choose the correct card from the number line, i.e. 4. Replace the cards and repeat, taking different cards.

ACTIVITY 5
Pairs

- *Adding 3-digit to 2-digit numbers*
Number cards (0 to 4) (PCM 1)
Use all the number cards to create a 3-digit number and a 2-digit number addition, e.g. 120 + 34, 120 + 43 ... Complete each addition. Find at least 20 different ways. Try to use a system. Are any of the totals the same?

ACTIVITY 1
Whole class, in pairs

- *Adding/subtracting multiples of 100 to/from 3-digit numbers*
A dice, interlocking cubes
Each pair writes down a 3-digit number. Throw the dice and write on the board the matching number of hundreds, e.g. the dice shows 3, write '300'. The children add or subtract that number of hundreds to or from the number they have written down. The pair whose answer is closest to 500 takes a cube. Continue until one pair has collected three cubes.

ACTIVITY 2
Pairs

- *Adding 3-digit numbers*
Two blank 3 × 3 grids (PCM 16)
Give each child a blank grid. One child writes a 3-digit number in the first space on his grid. The other child adds 204 to it and writes the answer in the corresponding space on her grid. They both check that the answer is correct. The second child now writes a new 3-digit number in another space on her grid. The first child adds 204 to it and writes the total in the corresponding space on his grid. They continue like this until all the spaces on their grids have a number.

ACTIVITY 3
4 children

- *Adding a 3-digit multiple of ten to a 3-digit number*
Place-value cards (hundreds, tens and units) (PCMs 10 to 12), a dice, post-it notes
Spread out the cards face down in three separate piles. One child throws the dice twice and creates a 3-digit number which is a multiple of ten, e.g. he throws a 5 and a 2 and makes 520 or 250. He writes this on the top of a post-it note. The other children each turn over a card from a different pile to create a 3-digit number. Working on their own, they add up the two numbers and write down their answer. Then they compare answers. Are they all the same? If not, they should work it out together. They write the total on the bottom of the post-it note and stick it on the three cards. Repeat with the children taking different roles.

ACTIVITY 4
3 children

- *Adding multiples of 100 to 3-digit numbers*
Number cards (1 to 5) (PCM 1), place-value cards (hundreds – except 500, tens and units) (PCMs 10 to 12)
Shuffle the place-value cards and place them in three piles face down. Lay out the number cards in a line face up along the top of the table. The children each take a card from a different pile and create a 3-digit number with them. They read the number together. They choose a card from the line and create a multiple of 100, e.g. if they choose 3, they make 300. Then they count on that many hundreds from their 3-digit number, writing down each number, including the first. E.g. if their 3-digit number is 475, and the card number is 3, they add 300 and write '475, 575, 675, 775'. They must agree the answer and then write down the matching addition, e.g. '475 + 300 = 775'. Repeat the activity several times.

ACTIVITY 5
Pairs

- *Adding and subtracting numbers*
A dice
The children throw the dice six times and write down the numbers. They create two 3-digit numbers with the numbers thrown and add them together. They then rearrange the digits of the two numbers so that the total is as large as possible, then rearrange the digits to make two numbers with the smallest possible total. What is the difference between the two additions? Repeat and see if the final difference is any larger.

N36 Number patterns

• *Recognising even and odd numbers*

A dice, interlocking cubes

Each pair decides whether to collect even or odd numbers. Sit the pairs in two groups, 'Odds' and 'Evens'. Throw the dice three times. Write on the board the numbers thrown. The children use these numbers to make a 3-digit number. They write down their number, trying to make the largest number of the type they are collecting. E.g. dice numbers 3, 1 and 4 – even 314, odd 431. Check each pair's number and, if it is the largest possible of their type, they take one cube. Repeat several times.

• *Recognising even and odd numbers*

Place-value cards (hundreds, tens and units) (PCMs 10 to 12), coins (10p), paper plate (for the bank)

Shuffle the place-value cards separately and place them in three piles face down. The children each start with ten 10p coins. They each guess whether the number will be even or odd. Each child takes a card from a different pile. They put the cards together and create a 3-digit number. They look to see if it is even or odd. Those who are correct put a coin back in the bank. Continue until someone has no more coins.

• *Counting in 50s*

Place-value cards (hundreds, tens and units) (PCMs 10 to 12), a dice

Spread out the cards face up in three separate lines. One child throws the dice. This is the starting number. The second child adds 50 to the starting number and uses the place-value cards to make the total, e.g. dice shows 4, so the second child makes 54. The children record this number. The third child adds 50 again, and uses the cards to make the total, i.e. 104. They record this number below the first. The children continue until they have written a list of numbers which reaches 1000 or over. Repeat.

• *Recognising odd and even numbers*

Number grid (1 to 100) (PCM 34), counters in three different colours

Each child has counters in only one colour. In turn, they place a counter on an even number on the grid. They continue until one of them has a line of four counters in a row with no counters of another colour breaking it up.

• *Recognising the patterns made by odd and even multiples*

The children work together to find whether there is a pattern of even and odd numbers when counting in 7s. Extend the activity by counting in 9s and then in 11s. Can the children explain their findings?

N37 Multiplication/division

ACTIVITY 1
Whole class, in pairs

- *Multiplying a 1-digit number by 10 and 100*
Number cards (1 to 9) (PCM 1), place-value board (H, T, U) (PCM 13) per pair
Shuffle the cards and place them face down in a pile. The children take turns to reveal a card, e.g. 3, and multiply it by 10, by placing it in the units column on the place-value board and sliding it one place to the left. They all write the resulting multiplication, i.e. '3 × 10 = 30'. When all the cards have been revealed, reshuffle them and repeat, this time multiplying by 100.

ACTIVITY 2
2-3 children

- *Multiplying a 1-digit number by 10 and 100*
Number cards (1 to 9) (PCM 1), Base Ten material (tens, hundreds)
Shuffle the cards and place them in a pile, face down. One child takes the top card, e.g. 7, and another collects a matching number of tens, i.e. 7 tens. Together they count the tens *Ten, twenty, thirty, ... seventy,* and then write the multiplication, i.e. '7 × 10 = 70'. Continue until all the cards have been revealed and the children have written nine multiplications. Repeat the activity, multiplying by 100, and collecting hundreds.

Ten, twenty, thirty, forty...

ACTIVITY 3
2-3 children

- *Multiplying a 2-digit number by 10*
- *Converting pence into pounds and pence*
Number cards (10 to 30) (PCMs 1 to 3), coins (£1, 10p)
Shuffle the cards and place them in a pile, face down. One child reveals a card, e.g. 17, and another collects a matching number of 10p coins. A third child changes any sets of ten 10p coins for a £1 coin. Finally, they all write down the multiplication, recording the answer in pence and pounds, i.e. '17 × 10p = 170p = £1.70'.

ACTIVITY 4
2-3 children

- *Multiplying a 2-digit number by 10*
Two sets of number cards (0 to 9) (PCM 1), place-value board (H, T, U) (PCM 13)
The cards are shuffled separately and placed, face down, in two piles. The children take turns to draw one card from each set to create a 2-digit number. They put the cards on the place-value board in their correct position, and then multiply them by 10, by sliding the digits one place to the left. All the children record the multiplication. Repeat for nine numbers.

ACTIVITY 5
2-3 children

- *Multiplying a 2-digit number by 10 and by 100*
- *Multiplying a 3-digit number by 10 and by 100*
Coins (£1, 10p, 1p), a cloth bag
The children place the 10p and 1p coins in the bag. They choose to multiply by 10 or 100 (or 1000). One child takes a handful of coins from the bag, e.g. 48p. They all write the multiplication, e.g. '48 × 100 = 4 800'. They check the multiplication by drawing a place-value board (Th, H, T, U) on paper, writing '48' in position then writing the new number beneath it when the digits have moved two places to the left. They have to say the number, i.e. *Four thousand eight hundred.* Replace the coins and repeat. Extend by adding the £1 coins to the bag. (Alternatively, use place-value cards instead of coins.)

Multiplication/division

ACTIVITY 1
Whole class, in pairs

- *Multiplying a multiple of 10 by a 1-digit number*
Number cards (10 to 50) (PCM 1 to 4), a dice (1 to 6), Base Ten material (hundreds, tens) (or interlocking cubes in towers of ten)
Shuffle the cards and place them face down in a pile. The children take turns to make a multiplication by revealing a card, e.g. 20, and multiplying it by a dice throw, e.g. 4. They check each other's answers by collecting tens, i.e. four lots of two tens (making eight tens, or 80). The children then write the multiplication. Repeat several times.

ACTIVITY 2
2-3 children

- *Multiplying 20 or 30 by a 1-digit number*
Squared paper, scissors
The children put coloured dots in several sets of 20 squares (in two rows of ten), and cut them out. They place two sets of 20 together, count the total number of squares and write '2 × 20 = 40'. They then add another set to write '3 × 20 = 60' and so on. They then extend this by colouring sets of 30 squares (in three rows of ten) and write different multiplications.

ACTIVITY 3
2-3 children

- *Multiplying a multiple of 10 by a 1-digit number*
Number cards (1 to 5) (PCM 1), tens cards (10 to 50) (PCM 8), Base Ten material (tens, hundreds)
Shuffle the cards separately and place them in two piles, face down. One child takes a tens card, e.g. 30. Another child takes a units card (for the multiplier), e.g. 3. Together they collect three 30s in Base Ten material i.e. 9 tens, changing ten tens into one hundred, where necessary. Finally, they write the multiplication, i.e. '3 × 30 = 90'.

ACTIVITY 4
2-3 children

- *Multiplying a multiple of 10 by a 1-digit number*
A dice (1 to 6), coins (10p), a cloth bag, Base Ten material (tens, hundreds), interlocking cubes
The coins are placed in the bag and one child takes out a handful, e.g. 40p. Another child throws the dice (for the multiplier), e.g. 5. All the children write the multiplication, i.e. '5 × 40', and attempt to record the answer. They check each other's answers with the Base Ten material, i.e. they collect five lots of four tens. All the children with the correct answer collect a cube. Repeat and continue the activity until one child has eight cubes.

ACTIVITY 5
3 children

- *Multiplying a multiple of 10 by a 1-digit number*
Place-value cards (tens and units) (PCM 10 to 12), a calculator, counters
The place-value cards are shuffled separately and placed face down in two piles. The children take turns to select one card from each pile, e.g. 20 and 9. The other two children multiply the two numbers together, writing down their answer, e.g. '20 × 9 = 180'. The third child checks the answer with the calculator. If they are correct, they take a counter. Repeat several times, with the children swapping roles. Who collects the most counters?

ACTIVITY 6
3 children

- *Finding pairs of factors of multiples of ten*
Calculator
One child writes a 3-digit multiple of ten, e.g. 240. The others find different ways to multiply two numbers together to make it, e.g. 24 × 10, 48 × 5, 120 × 2. They record all the multiplications. The first player uses a calculator to check. Repeat, swapping roles.

ACTIVITY 1
Whole class, in pairs

- *Multiplying by 4*

Number cards (1 to 10) (PCM 1), ×4 multiplication table (PCM 30)
Shuffle the cards and place them face down in a pile. The children take turns to reveal a card, e.g. 6, and say the number of fours, i.e. *Six fours are twenty-four.* They check by chanting the multiples of four using their fingers. Finally, they check using the ×4 table. Repeat several times.

ACTIVITY 2
2-3 children

- *Creating the ×4 multiplication table*

2 cm squared paper
The children write '1, 2, 3, 4' in a row on the squared paper, then '5, 6, 7, 8' in the second row, and so on. They write the multiplication table, writing '1 × 4 = 4' beside the first row, '2 × 4 = 8' beside the second row ... to complete the ×4 table.

ACTIVITY 3
2-3 children

- *Multiplying by 4*

Number grid 3 (PCM 19), blank 5×5 grid (PCM 18), calculator
The children work together to multiply each grid number by 4, and record the answers in the matching spaces on a blank grid. They use a calculator to check.

ACTIVITY 4
3-4 children

- *Recalling the ×4 multiplication facts*

Multiplication cards (×4) (PCM 26), interlocking cubes (towers of 4), counters
Shuffle the cards and place them in a pile face down. The children take turns to reveal a card, say and then write the resulting multiplication. They can use towers of four cubes to check. If they are correct, they take a counter. They check each other's answers. When all the cards have been used, start again.

ACTIVITY 5
2-3 children

- *Recalling the ×4 multiplication facts*
- *Linking ×4 multiplication facts to ÷4 division facts*

Multiplication/division cards (×4/÷4) (PCMs 26, 28, 29), interlocking cubes (towers of 4)
Shuffle the multiplication cards and place them in a pile, face down. Spread out the division cards, face up. The children take turns to reveal a multiplication card and say the answer. They can use towers of cubes to check. They then look for the matching division card. If correct, they take both cards and place them in front of them, side by side. Finally, they place all the cards in order, matching the multiplications with their divisions. Repeat.

ACTIVITY 6
3-4 children

- *Recognising the multiples of 4*
- *Linking ÷4 division facts to multiples of 4*

Number cards (1 to 40) (PCMs 1 to 4), a dice, counters (one colour each)
Place the cards in order, to form a number track. The children each place a counter on 1. They take turns to throw the dice and move a matching number of spaces along the track. If they land on a number in the ×4 table, e.g. 24, they leave the counter on that card, and say the matching division, i.e. *Twenty-four divided by four is six.* On their next turn, they continue with a new counter. When they all reach the end, the winner is the one with most counters on the track.

ACTIVITY 7
3-4 children

- *Multiplying by 4 by doubling then doubling again*

Number cards (10 to 30) (PCMs 1 to 3), a calculator, counters
Shuffle the cards and place them in a pile face down. One child turns over a card and all the children multiply the number by 4 (by doubling the number, then doubling again). Each child writes down their answer, then they check together using the calculator. Children with a correct answer collect a cube.

N40 Multiplication/division

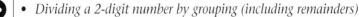

ACTIVITY 1
Whole class, in threes

• *Dividing a 2-digit number by grouping (including remainders)*
• *Linking multiplication/division facts*
30 counters or cubes per group, a dice
Throw the dice, e.g. 5. The children say how many groups of five counters can be made from the 30 counters. They check by grouping the counters. They write a multiplication and a division to match, i.e. '30 ÷ 5 = 6, 6 × 5 = 30'. Repeat, throwing the dice several times. Will the counters always divide exactly, or will there be a remainder? Repeat the activity, changing the number of counters.

ACTIVITY 2
3 children

• *Creating a division and matching multiplications*
Interlocking cubes, a calculator
The children take turns to arrange some cubes into groups of equal size, e.g. three groups of two. The other children say a multiplication and a division to match, i.e. *Three twos are six, six divided by two is three.* All the children write down the calculations.

ACTIVITY 3
2-4 children

• *Recalling division facts and matching multiplication facts*
Number cards (0 to 40) (PCMs 1 to 4), card for signs (×, ÷, =), interlocking cubes
The children arrange the cubes to make three fours (three towers of four cubes). They use the cards to create the matching multiplication, i.e. 3 × 4 = 12, and write it down. Then they exchange the '×' card for the '÷' card, rearranging the same number cards to make a division, i.e. 12 ÷ 4 = 3, and write it down. Repeat for several different multiplications.

ACTIVITY 4
3-4 children

• *Dividing a 2-digit number (up to 40) by a 1-digit number (including remainders)*
Number cards (10 to 40) (PCMs 1 to 4), a dice, interlocking cubes, counters
Shuffle the cards and place them in a pile, face down. The children take turns to reveal a card, e.g. 27, and to roll the dice, e.g. 4. All the children divide the card number by the dice number, recording any remainder, and write the answer down. They check each other's answers by building towers of four cubes to see how many groups make 27. All the children with a correct answer collect a counter. Continue until one child has collected eight counters.

ACTIVITY 5
2-3 children

• *Creating different divisions, each with the same given remainder*
Lists of multiples (×2, ×3, ×4, ×5, ×10)
The children create and write ten different divisions (dividing by 2, 3, 4, 5 or 10) each of which have a remainder of one. Extend this to ten divisions with a remainder of two, three, and so on. They can use the lists of multiples to check the divisions and the remainders. Extend to multiples of other numbers.

N41 Fractions

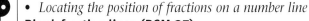

ACTIVITY 1
Whole class, in pairs

- *Locating the position of fractions on a number line*
Blank fraction lines (PCM 37)
The children mark the end of each line with 0 and 1. They label the markings on each line, as follows: the first line in thirds, the second in quarters, the third in sixths, the fourth in eighths and the fifth in tenths.

ACTIVITY 2
2+ children

- *Recognising pairs of equivalent fractions*
2 cm squared paper
The children draw and colour fraction strips. They illustrate halves, quarters and eighths by drawing four strips, eight squares long. They can use these to write pairs of matching (equivalent) fractions, e.g. '$\frac{2}{8} = \frac{1}{4}, \frac{4}{8} = \frac{2}{4}$...' The children can draw a similar set of fraction strips that are six squares long to illustrate thirds and sixths.

ACTIVITY 3
2-4 children

- *Recognising sets of equivalent fractions*
Fraction cards 1 (top section) and 3 (PCMs 31, 33)
The children sort the fraction cards into matching (equivalent) sets. They find how many matching sets there are, and how many are in each set. They write the matching fractions, e.g. '$\frac{1}{4} = \frac{2}{8}$'. Which fraction cards do not match any others?

ACTIVITY 4
2-3 children

- *Recognising sets of equivalent fractions*
Fraction cards 1, 2 and 3 (PCMs 31 to 33)
The children sort the fraction cards into matching (equivalent) sets (fraction cards with shaded shapes). They find how many matching sets there are, and how many are in each set. They write the matching fractions, e.g. '$\frac{1}{4} = \frac{2}{8}$'. Which fraction cards do not match any others?

ACTIVITY 5
2-4 children

- *Locating fractions on a number line*
- *Recognising the equivalence of fractions on a number line*
Blank fraction lines (PCM 37), squared paper
The children use their fraction lines from Activity 1 (or label the ends of each line 0 and 1). They mark the divisions on each line with the appropriate fraction and write any equivalent fractions above each marked fraction. For example, in the third line of PCM 37, they can write '$\frac{1}{3}$' above '$\frac{2}{6}$'. How many sets of equivalent fractions can they find? The children can extend the activity by drawing their own fraction line on squared paper, e.g. 12 units long, and marking fractions and equivalent fractions in the same way. Let them experiment with fractions on lines of different lengths, e.g. 20, 24, ...

N42 Addition

• *Adding a 2-digit number to a 3-digit number*
Two sets of place-value cards (tens) (PCM 12), interlocking cubes, scrap paper
Choose a target number, e.g. 500. Each pair writes down a 3-digit number less than the target number. Deal out one place-value card to each pair. They add this number to the number they have written down by adding the tens first. E.g. 345 + 70; they add 40 and 70 and get 110, then 300 + 110 + 5 which is 415. The pair whose total is nearest to the target number takes a cube. Discuss some of the answers. Repeat several times, changing the target number.

• *Adding two 3-digit numbers*
Place-value cards (hundreds, tens and units) (PCMs 10 to 12), coins (30 × 10p)
Shuffle the place-value cards separately and place them in three piles face down. Each child starts with ten 10p coins. The children take a card from each pile and make a 3-digit number. They add 111 to their number and write down the addition. When they have all finished, they check each other's addition. If they are correct, they place 10p in the centre. Repeat, taking another card each and adding 222. Extend this by adding 333 next time. They should try to continue until one child has no 10p coins.

• *Adding two 3-digit numbers*
Place-value cards (100 to 500, 10 to 50, 1 to 5) (PCMs 10, 12), a dice, coins (£1)
Shuffle the place-value cards separately and place them in three piles face down. Each child decides whether to collect odd or even numbers. They each take a card from a different pile, to make a 3-digit number. They throw the dice three times to create a second 3-digit number. They work together to add the two numbers, adding the hundreds, then the tens and then the units. Is the total even or odd? If the total matches the type of number they are collecting, they collect a £1 coin. Repeat several times.

• *Adding multiples of ten to 3-digit numbers*
10-division blank number line (PCM 36), tens cards (10 to 100) (PCM 8), post-it notes (small size, cut in half)
Shuffle the cards and place them in a pile face down. The children throw the dice three times to create a 3-digit number. One of them writes that number on a post-it and sticks it on the first mark on their number line. They then take a card and add that number to their 3-digit number. They do this by counting on in tens along the number line, stopping when they have added enough tens. They write the total on a post-it and stick it on the number line. They each write the addition, then repeat several times removing the old post-its. The children take turns to act as scribe.

• *Adding two 3-digit numbers*
Number grid 2 (PCM 17)
One child writes down two numbers from the grid that are together vertically or horizontally and adds them together. She shows her partner the answer, but not the numbers that were added. Her partner has to guess which two numbers were added. Repeat several times with the children taking different roles. (You may wish to have a time limit for guessing.)

N43 Addition

ACTIVITY 1
Whole class, in pairs

• *Adding 3-digit numbers using a vertical procedure*
Two sets of place-value cards (hundreds, tens and units) (PCMs 10 to 12), interlocking cubes
Each pair writes down two 3-digit numbers. Deal out one of each place-value card to each pair. The children create a 3-digit number using these cards. They add the three numbers using a vertical method. The pair whose total is nearest to 1000 takes a cube. Repeat several times.

ACTIVITY 2
3 children

• *Adding three 3-digit numbers*
Coins (1p, 10p, £1), paper for labels
The children each take an amount of money between £1 and £5. They each work out how much they have and label their pile. The children work together to add the three amounts vertically. They must all agree the total. They then combine the coins, and exchange ten 1p coins, if possible, for a 10p, and ten 10p coins, if possible, for a £1. How much do they have in total? Does it match their calculation? Repeat until they have completed six correct additions.

ACTIVITY 3
3 children

• *Adding 1-digit numbers to 3-digit numbers*
Place-value cards (hundreds, tens and units) (PCMs 10 to 12), number cards (1 to 9) (PCM 1), a calculator
Shuffle the place-value cards separately and place them in three piles face down. Spread the number cards out face down. The children each take a different place-value card to create one 3-digit number and each child writes it down. One child turns over a number card. The children write an addition, adding that 1-digit number to the 3-digit number. They agree the total and then check it using a calculator. If it is correct, they keep the cards, if not they put the cards back. Continue until all the number cards have gone.

ACTIVITY 4
Pairs

• *Adding three 4-digit numbers*
Number cards (1 to 9) (PCM 1)
The children use the cards to create two 4-digit numbers. They add the two numbers. What is the total? What is the largest total that can be achieved using these cards? What is the smallest total? Can the children make the total as close to 10000 as possible?

M1 Length

ACTIVITY 1
Whole class, in pairs

- *Estimating and measuring lengths accurately in centimetres*

A tape measure

Draw a line on the board and ask the children to estimate its length in centimetres. They write down their estimates. Choose two children to measure the length of the line and write it on the board. Which pair has the closest estimate? Repeat several times.

ACTIVITY 2
3-4 children

- *Estimating and measuring lengths in centimetres*

A ruler, ten pieces of string (1 cm, 2 cm ... 10 cm long), a cloth bag

Place all the strings in the bag. The children take turns to remove a piece of string and estimate its length. They then measure the string with the ruler. If they are correct they keep the string, otherwise it is put back in the bag. When all the strings have been removed who has the most pieces? Who has the longest string when all the pieces are placed together?

ACTIVITY 3
Pairs

- *Estimating and measuring lengths in metres and centimetres*

A metre rule, sticky tape

One child lies down on the floor. Another child places some tape at his feet and some tape at his head. The two children then work together to measure the length between the tape using the metre rule. They should write the length in metres and centimetres. The second child then lies on the floor and the process is repeated. The first child then stretches his arms as wide as he can while the other child measures the distance from finger tip to finger tip. They write this length in metres and centimetres. The second child then stretches his arms and the process is repeated. Are the children wider than they are long?

ACTIVITY 4
3 children

- *Estimating and measuring in centimetres*

A ruler

The children take turns to find an object in the classroom, e.g. a book. They each write an estimate of its length in centimetres. They then measure the object carefully and agree its length. The child with the closest estimate scores three points. After five rounds, who has the most points? Can they find a set of objects which measure 100 cm in total?

ACTIVITY 5
3 children

- *Relating metres and kilometres*

Two sets of place-value cards (hundreds, tens and units) (PCMs 10 to 12), a calculator

Shuffle the cards separately and place them in three piles face down. The children each take three cards (one from each pile) and create a 3-digit number. This represents a distance in metres. Each child has to say how many metres she has. The children work together to work out the total of all three distances. (They may use a calculator if necessary.) How close is the total to one kilometre? The children write down the total distance, e.g. 932 m, and also whether it is more or less than one kilometre. E.g. they write '932 km – a bit less', or '1385 km – a lot more'. They then each take three new card and repeat.

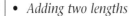 **M2** Length

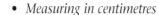

ACTIVITY 1
Whole class, in pairs

- *Adding two lengths*
- *Working out the difference between one length and another*

Books of different lengths

Choose three books and show the children each one. Ask them how long a line they think the three books will make if they are placed end to end on the table (or shelf). Each pair estimates a total length and writes it down. Measure each book and write its length on the board. The children add the three lengths and find the total. They then calculate the difference between their estimate and the actual total. Check the total length by demonstrating how to measure the three lengths correctly. Which pair made the closest estimate? Did they perform their calculations correctly? Repeat the process with three different books.

ACTIVITY 2
3-4 children

- *Measuring in centimetres around different objects*

A tape measure (marked in cm), a plate, a large pot, a teddy bear, other objects

The children choose an object to measure around. They each write an estimate in centimetres of what they think the measurement will be. Taking a large pot as an example, one child holds the start of the tape measure in place while a second child winds it around the pot. A third child reads the measurement in centimetres and the children write down the actual length. They compare this with their estimates. The children choose another object and repeat the process.

ACTIVITY 3
3 children

- *Measuring accurately in centimetres*
- *Finding a total number of lengths*
- *Finding differences between lengths*

Paper strips, scissors, a metre stick (marked in cm)

The children use the metre stick to measure their arm-span, cubit (the length from their elbow to finger-tip) and stride. Using paper strips and then the metre stick, they also measure their head and wrist circumferences. Then they each find the total of their body lengths. Whose total is the largest, whose is the smallest? Does the tallest person have the longest arm span?

ACTIVITY 4
2 children

- *Measuring in centimetres*
- *Relating units of length to solve problems*

A tape measure (marked in cm)

The children measure the length of each other's stride. They work together to find how many strides each would make in 10 metres. How many in 100 metres? How many in 1000 metres? How many in a mile (1600 metres)?

ACTIVITY 5
Pairs

- *Finding the difference between two lengths*
- *Relating units of length to solve problems*

A consumer catalogue (for furniture)

The children take turns to look in the catalogue and choose two similar items of furniture, e.g. two sofas, two bookcases. They calculate the difference in length between the items. They do this five times, keeping a running total of their differences.

M3 Time

ACTIVITY 1
Whole class, in pairs

• *Finding the interval between two times within one hour*
An analogue clock with moveable hands, Blu-tack
Each pair writes down four multiples of five between 5 and 60. Take the clock and move the long hand to a number. Place a piece of Blu-tack on a number further round the clock. Ask the class, *How many minutes are there to the Blu-tack from where the long hand is pointing?* The children count round from the hand to the Blu-tack in fives. Has any pair written down this number? If so, they cross it out. Continue until one pair has crossed out all of their numbers.

ACTIVITY 2
3 children

• *Telling the time to quarter of an hour*
An analogue clock with moveable hands, a coin, interlocking cubes
The children set the clock to 12 o'clock. They take turns to spin the coin. If it lands heads, they move one quarter around the clock. If it lands tails, they move two quarters around the clock. They read the time shown and the other children check. If a child passes 'o'clock' in their go, they take a cube. Continue until one child has five cubes.

ACTIVITY 3
3 children

• *Finding the interval between two times within one hour*
Number cards (1 to 12) (PCMs 1, 2), analogue clock face sheet (PCM 41), two counters (one red, one blue)
Shuffle the cards and place them face down in a pile. The children take turns to remove two cards and place the counters on the matching numbers on the clock, e.g. 5 and 9. The other two children calculate the difference between the two positions, i.e. 20 minutes. Then all the children record the two cards as times, i.e. twenty-five minutes past and forty-five minutes past, and the time interval, i.e. 20 minutes. They replace the cards at random in the pile and play five more rounds.

ACTIVITY 4
3-4 children

• *Finding the interval between two times within one hour*
Digital time cards (PCM 40), interlocking cubes, an analogue clock
Shuffle the cards and place them face down in a pile. The children take turns to select two cards at random, e.g. 4:40 and 4:25. They calculate the time interval and say it aloud. The other children check using the analogue clock. If a child is correct she collects a cube. The cards are replaced and the next child plays.

ACTIVITY 5
Pairs

• *Calculating a time interval*
An analogue clock with moveable hands
The children each write a time between 12 o'clock and 3 o'clock and hide it from their partner. They make a note of their own time, then swap their first papers with their partner. They each calculate the difference in minutes between the two times, then compare answers. If they disagree, they can use the clock to help. Repeat several times.

ACTIVITY 6
Pair

• *Telling the time to quarter of an hour*
Concept keyboard with word processor (create overlay and file to match)
The teacher creates an overlay with written times (quarter to, eight fifteen,...) on the left side and several digital and analogue clock times on the right side. The child has to press the time on the left and then the correct clock. If they select the wrong clock a message tells them to try again.

ACTIVITY 7
3-4 children

• *Recognising the number of minutes in an hour*
Game 6: 'Just a minute', counters, dice, cubes
(See the instructions on the card.)

Time

ACTIVITY 1
Whole class, in pairs

- *Solving simple problems*
- *Telling the time to five-minute intervals*

An analogue clock with moveable hands, a dice, interlocking cubes
Each pair writes down a digital time, e.g. 4:35. Set the hands on the analogue clock, e.g. at quarter past two. Throw the dice. The number thrown indicates the number of five minute intervals to add to that time. E.g. you throw a 5 and the children add five fives (twenty-five minutes) to the time on the clock. Point at the analogue clock. What time will it be twenty-five minutes later than this? Encourage each pair to work this out, and then show them how to reach the answer. Write the analogue time on the board, e.g. 'twenty to three'. What time will the digital clock show? Write the digital equivalent on the board, e.g. '2:40'. Does any pair have a matching time? Repeat several times.

ACTIVITY 2
3 children

- *Telling the time to five-minute intervals*

An analogue clock with moveable hands, counters
One child writes down a time and shows it to another child, who sets it on the clock face. The third child looks at the clock and writes the matching time. The first and third child compare the times they have written down. If they match, the second child takes a counter. The children repeat, swapping roles, for six rounds.

ACTIVITY 3
3-4 children

- *Telling the time in five-minute intervals*
- *Adding five or ten minutes to a time*

An analogue clock face with moveable hands, counters, a coin
Set the clock to 3 o'clock. The children take turns to spin the coin. If it lands heads, they move the long hand forwards five minutes. If it lands tails, they move the long hand forwards ten minutes. They say the new time aloud. If a child passes 'o'clock' he collects a counter. The winner is the first child to collect two counters.

ACTIVITY 4
2 children

- *Telling the time and solving simple time problems*

Digital time cards (PCM 40), number cards (1 to 60) (PCMs 1 to 5)
Shuffle the cards separately and place them face down in two piles. The children take turns to select a time card and write down the time. They then choose a number card and calculate the time that many minutes later. They record the new time, checking each other's work. When all the time cards have been used, reshuffle them and repeat, this time calculating the time that many minutes earlier.

ACTIVITY 5
4 children

- *Finding the difference between pairs of times*

Each child writes a time which is a multiple of five minutes (e.g. 1:20, 5:35) and hides it from the others. They reveal their times, then work together to calculate the difference between each of the times (there are six differences altogether). Repeat with four new times.

ACTIVITY 6
Pair

- *Telling the time to five-minute intervals*

Concept keyboard with word processor (create overlay and file to match)
The teacher creates an overlay with written times (ten to, ten past …) on the left side and several digital and analogue clock times on the right side. The child has to press the time on the left and then the correct clock. If they select the wrong clock a message tells them to try again.

Capacity

ACTIVITY 1
Whole class

- *Measuring capacity in litres and millilitres*
- *Recognising the relationship between millilitres and litres*

A bucket, a litre measure (calibrated in 100 millilitres), water

The children discuss how many litres and millilitres of water will fill the bucket. Record their guesses. They take turns to fill the litre measure and tip it into the bucket, counting as they do so. When the bucket is nearly full, they may have to tip in less than a litre, e.g. 400 millilitres. Write the measured capacity of the bucket. Who had the closest guess? Extend by using the litre measure to fill other large container.

ACTIVITY 2
3-4 children

- *Measuring capacity in millilitres*
- *Reading a scale*

A variety of containers (all less than $\frac{1}{2}$ litre), a measuring jug (calibrated in 100 millilitres), a dry filler (e.g. lentils)

The children estimate the capacity of four containers and place them in order. They then fill the four containers with the dry filler. Using the jug, they measure how much each one holds. Which holds the most? Which holds the least? They place the four containers in order, from smallest to largest, draw them and write the amount each one holds, e.g. 'mug holds 300 ml'. Were their estimates close? Repeat with different containers.

ACTIVITY 3
2-3 children

- *Measuring capacity using a 100 ml container*
- *Beginning to recognise the relationship between 100 millilitres and 1 litre*

A 100 ml container (e.g. yoghurt pot), a litre measuring jug (calibrated in 100 millilitres), a dry filler (e.g. lentils), counters

The children discuss how many yoghurt pots of dry filler will fill the litre jug and record their guesses. They take turns to fill the pot with lentils and tip it into the jug. They take one counter each time they empty the pot. When the jug is full, how many counters do they have altogether? (They should have ten.) How close were their estimates? Extend by estimating for other containers (how many to fill the litre jug?).

ACTIVITY 4
3-4 children

- *Estimating and measuring capacity in litres and $\frac{1}{2}$ litres*

A large plastic bottle (at least 2 litres), containers (1 litre and $\frac{1}{2}$ litre), dry filler, crayons or felt-tipped pens

The children fill the $\frac{1}{2}$ litre container with lentils. They guess where the $\frac{1}{2}$ litre of lentils would come to if emptied into the large bottle. They each mark their guess on the bottle, then check by emptying the lentils into it. Who was closest? They repeat for 1 litre, $1\frac{1}{2}$ litres and 2 litres.

M6 Time

ACTIVITY 1
Whole class, in pairs

- *Estimating, using the knowledge that there are 24 hours in a day*
- *Solving simple problems*

Number cards (4 to 12) (PCMs 1, 2), interlocking cubes

Take a card and write that number of days on the board, e.g. '4'. Each pair has to guess the number of hours in that number of days. They write down their estimate, then calculate it together *Four twenties are eighty, four fours are sixteen, ninety-six altogether*. Any pair who is correct, takes a cube. Repeat several times. When all the cards have been taken, who has the most cubes?

ACTIVITY 2
4 children

- *Recognising that a day has 24 hours*

Cards for labels (Monday to Sunday), a dice, interlocking cubes

Spread out the cards face up on the table. The children take turns to throw the dice and collect a matching number of cubes. Each cube represents one hour. When a child has collected 24 hours, he chooses a day. The winner is the first child to collect two days.

ACTIVITY 3
3-4 children

- *Recognising that there are 60 minutes in an hour*

A dice, interlocking cubes

Each child takes turns to throw the dice. He writes down that number of five minutes. E.g. he throws a 4 and write down four lots of five, i.e. '20 minutes'. The children have several throws each. If a child collects more than 60 minutes, he takes a cube to represent an hour. The winner is the first child to collect five hours. (Alternatively, you could use 20 circles divided into 5-minute sections, the children place counters on the sections to complete circles/hours.)

ACTIVITY 4
3 children

- *Ordering the days of the week*

Card for labels (Monday to Sunday), cubes

Shuffle the cards and deal them so that each child has two and one is left face down. The child holding Monday places it face up in the centre of the table. She then takes the spare card. The child to her left must place Tuesday, if she has it, face up next to Monday. If she can't play, she takes a cube. Play continues like this until all the days are lined up in order, Monday to Sunday. The child with the fewest cubes wins.

ACTIVITY 5
Pairs

- *Solving problems relating hours to minutes to seconds*

A calculator

Ask the children to think about the time in a school week. They should work out: how many days they are at school, how many hours in each school day, and how many minutes. They can use a calculator, if necessary.

ACTIVITY 6
Pair

- *Ordering the days of the week*

Concept keyboard with word processor (create an overlay and file to match)

The overlay should have the days of the week and the words 'is the day before', 'and' and 'is the day after'. The pupil press the day of the week and then the appropriate phrases to make a correct sentence.

Saturday		Wednesday
	Tuesday	Thursday
	Friday	
Sunday		Monday

| is the day before | and | is the day after |

49

(M7) Weight

ACTIVITY 1
2-3 children

- *Weighing objects in units of 100 g*
- *Beginning to estimate the weight of objects in units of 100 g*

A rocker balance, a variety of small packets/packages/jars, weights (10 × 100 g, 1 × 1 kg)

The children work together to weigh each packet, package or jar. They first guess how many hundred grams each one will weigh. The children weigh each in turn, using the 100 g weights. They then write the name of each packet with its weight and compare it to their original estimate.

ACTIVITY 2
2-3 children

- *Matching sets of objects to weights of 100 g, 200 g, … 1 kg*

A rocker balance, wooden bricks, weights (10 × 100 g)

The children place one 100 g weight on one side of the balance and on the other side, enough wooden bricks to equal the weight. They write '100 g', alongside the number of bricks. They add another 100 g weight to the balance and add more wooden bricks to equal 200 g. They then write '200 g', with the number of bricks. The children continue until they weigh 1000 g of bricks. (They may need to calculate the last few if there are not enough bricks.)

ACTIVITY 3
3-4 children

- *Identifying objects in units of 100 g*

A balance, weights (10 × 100 g), objects to weigh

The children find an object, or set of objects, which weighs between 100 g and 200 g. The object is placed on the balance and has to be shown to be, less than 200 g and more than 100 g. The results are recorded, e.g. 'book → between 100 g and 200 g'. They continue finding objects that weigh between 200 g and 300 g, between 300 g and 400 g, …

ACTIVITY 4
3-4 children

- *Weighing objects in units of 100 g*
- *Matching 1 kg with different sets of weights*

A balance, weights (10 × 100 g), 6 freezer bags and ties (or 6 identical containers with lids, or paper bags), sand

The children measure 100 g of sand and pour it into a freezer bag, tie it and label it. They do the same for bags of 200 g, 300 g, 400 g, 500 g and 1 kg of sand. They test the weights of the bags of sand by balancing different bags with the 1 kg of sand, e.g. 100 g + 200 g + 300 g + 400 g.

M8 Time

ACTIVITY 1
Whole class, in pairs

- *Ordering the months of the year*
Number cards (1 to 12) (PCMs 1, 2)
Shuffle the cards and place them in a pile face down. Each pair writes down the name of four months. Turn over a card and read out the number. Which month is that in the year? The children work it out and see if they have that month written down. Work out together which month it is and agree the answer. E.g. card 5 is chosen so the month is May. Any pair with that month written down may cross it off. Continue until one pair has crossed off all four months.

ACTIVITY 2
3-4 children

- *Ordering the months of the year*
Card for labels (January to December), interlocking cubes
Shuffle the cards and deal them out so that each child has the same amount. The child holding January places it face up in the centre of the table. The child to her left must place February, if she has it, face up next to January. If she can't play, she takes a cube. Play continues like this until all the months are lined up in order, January to December. The child with the fewest cubes wins.

ACTIVITY 3
4 children

- *Using the calendar to solve simple problems*
A current calendar
One child turns to the month of their birthday, e.g. May. The others each guess and write down the date of the child's birthday, e.g. '4th May', '19th May', '26th May'. The first child finds his birthday on the calendar and shows the others. The children work out how many days there are from their guess to the birthday, or how many days from the birthday to their guess. They check each other's calculation. The children repeat the process, with another child choosing their birthday month, until they have all had a turn.

ACTIVITY 4
Pairs

- *Solving problems by relating days, weeks and years*
A calculator
The children work out roughly how many days old they are, using their knowledge of how many days there are in a week and how many weeks there are in a year. They can use a calculator to help them, if necessary. (Ignore leap years if necessary.)

ACTIVITY 5
Pairs

- *Solving problems relating months and years*
A calculator
The children find how many months old they are, using their knowledge of how many months there are in a year. They need to work out the months in the number of full years first, then add the extra months. They can use a calculator to help them, if necessary.

ACTIVITY 6
Pair

- *Ordering the months of the year*
Concept keyboard with word processor (create an overlay and file to match)
The overlay should have the months of the year and the words 'is the month before', 'and', and 'is the month after'. The pupils press the month of the year and then the appropriate phrases to make a correct sentence.

S1 2-d shape

ACTIVITY 1
Whole class, in threes

- *Constructing and naming 2-d shapes*
Coloured paper, scissors
The children fold and cut the coloured paper to make straight-lined shapes. They label each shape with its name. They should try to make ten different shapes.

ACTIVITY 2
3 children

- *Sorting 2-d shapes based on number of sides, naming 2-d shapes*
Shape cards (sheets 1 and 2) (PCMs 42, 43)
The children count the number of sides on each shape on the cards. They sort the cards into sets that have the same number of sides. Finally, they name the shapes in each set.

ACTIVITY 3
3-4 children

- *Recognising and naming 2-d shapes*
Plastic 2-d shapes (including quadrilaterals – squares and rectangles, not quadrilaterals – triangles, pentagons, hexagons, octagons), card for shape labels, a cloth bag
Spread out the shape labels, face up, on the table. Place the shapes in the bag. The children take turns to remove a shape from the bag and place it beside its label. Use the 'quadrilateral' label first, then replace it with 'square' and 'rectangle'.

ACTIVITY 4
3-4 children

- *Recognising and naming 2-d shapes*
Shape cards (sheets 1 and 2) (PCMs 42, 43), counters
Shuffle the cards, and deal one to each child. The children who are dealt a quadrilateral collect a counter and together they check the names of the other shapes. Deal another card, then another, and so on until they have all been dealt. Reshuffle the cards and repeat, but this time the children collect a counter for each hexagon that is dealt. Continue playing, focusing on a different shape each round. Who is the first to collect eight counters?

ACTIVITY 5
3-4 children

- *Constructing 2-d shapes, recognising and using the vocabulary related to 2-d shapes*
Straight edge shapes, a cloth bag
The shapes are placed in the 'feely' bag. The children take turns to feel a shape in the bag, and describe it. The others draw it from the description. Are the shapes the same? The children continue, sharing the different roles.

ACTIVITY 6
3-4 children

- *Constructing and naming 2-d shapes*
Sheets of card, sheets of paper, scissors, paint
The children fold a sheet of card, cut out a shape along the fold line using straight line cuts, and then open out the card. They place this on top of a sheet of paper, and make a copy of the shape by painting over the hole. They then write the name of the shape next to it and any other facts they know about the shape.

ACTIVITY 7
Pairs

- *Recognising and naming 2-d shapes, including number of sides*
Concept keyboard with word processor (create an overlay and file to match)
The overlay should have graphics of the shapes. When the shape is pressed, the name of the shape will appear; the children will press the appropriate number of sides. After the children collect the printout, they should draw or stick appropriate shapes beside the sentences. (The children could make it up into a book for the infant classes.)

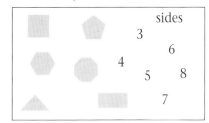

Symmetry

ACTIVITY 1

Whole class, in pairs

• *Recognising the different lines of symmetry on a square*

Square sheets of paper

The children fold their square in different ways and explore its lines of symmetry. They can draw the lines on the square. How many different lines are there?

ACTIVITY 2

Pairs

• *Locating lines of symmetry in shapes by folding*

Two copies of shape sheet 1 (enlarged to A3) (PCM 42), scissors

The children each cut out the same shape and investigate it for lines of symmetry by folding. They discuss the symmetry of the shape to see if they agree. They repeat for each of the other shapes. They sort the cut-out shapes according to their number of lines of symmetry. They then make a display of the shapes, naming each one and drawing lines to indicate the lines of symmetry. (If necessary limit the cards by using only six shapes.)

ACTIVITY 3

2-4 children

• *Locating lines of symmetry in shapes by folding, naming common 2-d shapes*

Plastic 2-d shapes (including squares, rectangles, triangles, pentagons, hexagons, octagons), sheets of paper, scissors

The children use the shapes as templates. They draw around each one and cut out the paper shapes. They test the shapes for lines of symmetry by folding them and colouring any lines of symmetry they find. They then name the shapes and use them to form a display. Finally, they sort the plastic shapes according to the number of lines of symmetry.

ACTIVITY 4

2-3 children

• *Locating lines of symmetry using a mirror*

Two copies of the shape cards sheets 1 and 2 (PCMs 42, 43), plastic mirrors

Using one set of shape cards, the children sort the cards according to whether or not the shapes have lines of symmetry. They then sort the symmetrical shapes according to how many lines of symmetry each has. They use a mirror to check. The children then draw the lines of symmetry on the other sheet of shape cards.

ACTIVITY 5

1-2 children

• *Drawing and colouring symmetrical shapes*

KidPix software

Using KidPix, the children select the symmetry option from the 'wacky brush' tool. The children draw a symmetrical shape and then colour it in symmetrically. This can either be done within KidPix, or printed out and coloured with pens or crayons.

ACTIVITY 6

Pairs

• *Drawing symmetrical shapes*

Plastic mirrors, ruler

Each child draws a straight line (the line of symmetry) on a piece of paper and then draws half a shape or picture, up to the line. They swap paper and draw the other half of their partner's shape. They then use mirrors to check.

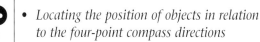 **S3 Direction**

ACTIVITY 1
Whole class

- *Locating the position of objects in relation to the four-point compass directions*
A paper compass fixed to point north
The children take turns to play a version of eye-spy in the classroom. With the help of the compass, they say *I spy something between east and south.* The other guess what it might be.

ACTIVITY 2
2-3 children

- *Locating objects lying in the four-point compass directions*
A direction compass
The children choose a starting point, and locate north. They write down some objects in the classroom and some outside the classroom which lie in each of the four directions. They repeat the activity from a different starting position.

ACTIVITY 3
3 children

- *Using a programmable toy to move in the four-point compass directions*
Roamer (pre-programmed to turn in right angles), turning cards (PCM 38)
Shuffle the cards and place them face down in a pile. The children take turns to reveal a card and program the Roamer to turn, left or right, the number of angles required. The next child starts from the new position.

ACTIVITY 4
4 children

- *Recognising the four-point compass directions*
Game 7: 'Falling in the water', direction cards (PCM 39), a dice (numbered 1, 2, 3 twice), counters
(See instructions on the card.)

ACTIVITY 5
Pairs

- *Constructing a map, positioning objects so that they relate to each other in directions determined by the four-point compass directions*
- *Describing the direction of one object from another using the four-point compass directions*
Squared paper
The children draw a 'Treasure Island' map with some landmarks (e.g. treasure, cave) and mark the four compass directions on the map. They should try to make some of the landmarks north, south, east or west of each other. They then write alongside the map the direction of the landmarks from each other, e.g. 'cave to treasure: south; camp to cave: west'.

ACTIVITY 6
3-4 children

- *Using the four-point compass directions to describe and record a route*
LOGO software, Treasure Island (PCM 44)
This activity assumes that the children already know how to use LOGO. An acetate sheet is attached to the computer monitor (see PCM 44). The children are given a record sheet (as shown). They follow the route to the treasure and record the directions in which they travel.

Starting point	Where to?	Compass direction	Distance

3-d shape

ACTIVITY 1
Whole class

- *Sorting prisms according to the shape of their end-faces*
A set of prisms, a cloth bag
Place the prisms in the bag. The children take turns to feel for a prism, name the end-face, then remove it to check. If they are correct they keep it. Otherwise they replace it in the bag. They continue until all prisms have been removed.

ACTIVITY 2
2-3 children

- *Recognising prisms*
A set of 3-d shapes (including some prisms), a cloth bag, counters
Place the shapes in the bag. The children take turns to remove a shape, searching for a prism. If it is a prism, they collect a counter. Who has the most counters when all the shapes have been removed?

ACTIVITY 3
3-4 children

- *Constructing prisms*
3-d model-making materials (e.g. Polydron, Clixi), blank labels
Using the model-making materials, the children investigate making different prisms. They then make labels to describe the faces, e.g. 2 hexagons, 6 squares.

ACTIVITY 4
3-4 children

- *Sorting prisms according to their number of faces*
Two sets of number cards (1 to 10) (PCM 1), a set of prisms, a cloth bag
Put the prisms in the bag. The children take turns to remove a shape, count the number of faces, and place a matching number card alongside each one.

ACTIVITY 5
Pairs

- *Classifying prisms according to the shape of their faces*
A set of prisms, card for 3-d shape labels (cube, cuboid, cylinder, pyramid, sphere, cone), blank card for labelling the face shapes
The children investigate the shapes of the faces of each prism, placing an appropriate label by each one. They then draw a table to show the results.

S5 3-d shape

ACTIVITY 1
Whole class in 2 groups

• *Recognising the names of common 3-d shapes*
3-d shape names (written on the board), set of 3-d shapes, cloth bag
Place the shapes in the bag. Sit the children in two groups and choose one child from each group to sit at the front. Reveal a shape. The first child to put up her hand goes to the board and points to the shape name. If correct her group scores a point. If not the other child has a go. If neither is correct the shape is returned to the bag. Choose another two children for the next shape.

ACTIVITY 2
3-4 children

• *Sorting 3-d shapes according to number of faces, edges and vertices*
A set of 3-d shapes, blank labels
The children order the shapes according to the number of faces each has, i.e. they place the shapes in a straight line, so that those with the fewest faces are on the left and those with the most are on the right. The children take turns to make labels, one for each shape, e.g. 'cuboid: 6 faces'. They then re-order the shapes based on the number of vertices they have, and label them. Finally, they do the same based on the number of edges.

ACTIVITY 3
2-3 children

• *Recognising the names of common 3-d shapes*
A set of 3-d shapes, card for 3-d shape labels (cube, cuboid, pyramid, sphere, cone, cylinder)
The children sort the shapes according to their names. They place them alongside the matching name label. Finally, they try to describe the properties of each set of shapes.

ACTIVITY 4
3-4 children

• *Counting the number of faces, edges and vertices of different 3-d shapes*
A set of different-shaped boxes, blank labels
The children write labels to indicate the number of faces, edges and vertices of each box. They discuss the name of each shape. What is the most common box shape? Why?

ACTIVITY 5
3-4 children

• *Constructing 3-d shapes*
• *Counting the number of faces, edges and vertices of different 3-d shapes*
3-d model-making materials (e.g. Polydron, Clixi), blank labels
Using six pieces of the materials, the children experiment by constructing different shapes which have six faces. They write labels, one for each shape, e.g. '6 faces, 12 edges, 8 vertices'. Repeat the activity for shapes with eight faces.

ACTIVITY 6
2-3 children

• *Constructing 3-d shapes*
• *Counting the number of faces, edges and vertices of different 3-d shapes*
Straws, pipe-cleaners, blank labels
The children construct cubes, cuboids, prisms etc. using the straws and pipe-cleaners. They label each shape, e.g. '7 faces, 15 edges, 10 vertices' and display the shapes and labels.

S6 Angle

ACTIVITY 1
Whole class in pairs

• *Recognising right angles*
Number cards (1 to 6) (PCM 1) per pair, analogue clock with moveable hands
Set the clock so the minute hand is pointing at 12. Rotate the minute hand through a given number of right angles, e.g. 3. The children hold up a number card to match the number of right angles turned. Repeat several times, choosing different starting positions.

ACTIVITY 2
2-3 children

• *Recognising right angles in 2-d shapes*
Two copies of the shape cards (PCMs 42, 43), right angle measures (made by folding a piece of paper in half, then in half again and marking the right angle corner)
Spread out one set of the cards face up on the table. The children use the right angle measures to count the number of right angles in each shape. They sort the cards into sets: shapes which have no right angles, shapes which have one right angle, shapes which have two right angles, etc. They then record the right angles on the other set of shape card sheets.

ACTIVITY 3
2-3 children

• *Recognising and measuring angles which are more than, less than or exactly a right angle*
Right angle measures (as for Activity 2), ruler, scissors
Using the right angle measures, the children draw and then cut out angles. They create some angles that are less than a right angle and colour them blue, some that are more than a right angle and colour them yellow, and some that are exactly a right angle and colour them red.

ACTIVITY 4
2-3 children

• *Recognising right angle turns, clockwise and anticlockwise*
Turning cards (PCM 38)
Shuffle the cards and place them face down in a pile. The children decide on a starting point to face before making each turn, e.g. the door. They take turns to pick a card, and without showing it to the others, perform the turn. The other children describe the turn, then check the card to see if they are correct.

ACTIVITY 5
2 children

• *Using a programmable toy to make right angle turns to create shapes*
Roamer (pre-programmed to turn in right angles), pen
The children devise a series of instructions to make the Roamer trace out a capital E, F or H.

ACTIVITY 6
2-3 children

• *Constructing and describing right angle turns, clockwise and anticlockwise*
An analogue clock with moveable hands, turning cards (PCM 38)
Shuffle the cards and place them face down in a pile. One child sets the clock at a particular 'quarter' of an hour, i.e. the minute hand points to 12, 3, 6 or 9, and says the time. The children take turns to reveal a card, turn the minute hand according to the card, then say the new time. They check each other's moves.

Angle

ACTIVITY 1
Whole class in groups of 4

• *Making right-angle turns described in relation to the four-point compass*
Turning cards (PCM 38), paper compass (made in the Teacher Card), direction cards (PCM 39), a pointer, counters, one set per group
Shuffle the turning cards and place them face down in a pile. Each child chooses a direction card: N, S, E or W. They start with the pointer pointing at north on the paper compass. The first child picks a turning card and performs a matching turn with the pointer. The card is replaced at random in the pile. The child whose direction card matches the finishing position collects a counter. The next child starts from the new position. The winner is the first to collect eight counters.

ACTIVITY 2
3 children

• *Describing right angle turns in relation to the four-point compass*
A direction compass
The children choose a starting point in the classroom, and locate north with the help of the compass. They write down three objects in the classroom which lie in each of the four directions. They take turns to face north, and choose a listed object. The other two children describe the necessary turn to face the object, e.g. *Turn clockwise through one right angle.*

ACTIVITY 3
4 children

• *Following instructions based on clockwise and anticlockwise turns, and the four-point compass directions*
Game 8: 'Four points', direction cards (PCM 39), a dice, a pointer
(See instructions on the card.)

ACTIVITY 4
2 children

• *Creating a journey based on using the four-point compass directions*
Roamer (pre-programmed to turn in right angles, step length 1 decimetre), a direction compass, a set of objects (e.g. boxes)
Arrange the objects in an open space. Find north with the compass, and mark 'H' for harbour on the ground beyond the objects. The children start with the Roamer pointing north. Can they steer the 'ship' around the 'icebergs' to reach the harbour safely? They should record their route, substituting left/right turns with appropriate compass directions.

S8 Position

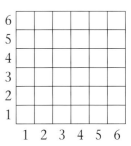

ACTIVITY 1

Whole class or 4 children

• *Locating position on a squared grid*

Shape cards (sheets 1 and 2) (PCMs 42, 43), two dice, counters, A3 paper with large 6 × 6 grid drawn on it

Place the shape cards on the grid at random. The children label the columns and rows as shown. They take turns to throw the dice, one at a time, the first dice representing the column number and the second dice representing the row number. If a shape lies in the matching cell, the child collects counters to match the number of sides of the shape. The winner is the first to collect 20 counters. (For the whole class activity draw one grid on the board and group the children in two or more teams.)

ACTIVITY 2

3 children

• *Describing the position of objects on a squared grid*

Blank 5×5 grid (PCM 18)

The children label the columns A to E (up the left side), and the rows 1 to 5 (along the bottom). They draw shapes or objects inside different squares on the grid. Alongside the grid, they then write the name of each object and describe its position using the letters and numbers. (This could be extended into a form of the game 'Battleships', using one grid per child. The children have to guess the positions of their opponents shapes.)

ACTIVITY 3

4 children

• *Locating position on a squared grid*

A3 paper with a large blank 6 × 6 grid drawn on it, a pack of playing cards (aces to nines), two dice

Label the columns and rows on the grid 1 to 6. Place the 36 playing cards at random in the 36 cells of the grid. The children decide which of the four suits of cards each one will collect. They take turns to throw the dice, one at a time, the first dice representing the column number and the second dice representing the row number. If one of their cards lies in the matching position, they take it. The winner is the first to collect three cards of any one suit.

ACTIVITY 4

2 pairs

• *Locating position on a squared grid*

Blank 5×5 grid, one per pair (PCM 18)

Label the columns of the grids A to E and the rows 1 to 5. One pair secretly draws ten stars at random on their grid (only one star per cell). The other pair tries to guess where the stars are hidden. They identify a cell on the grid by saying a column letter and a row number, to which the response is either *Hit!* or *Miss!* After each guess, they record the guess position on their grid and take a counter. They continue guessing until they have secured five hits. How many guesses did they make? (Check the number of counters.) Repeat, swapping roles

D1 Tally charts

ACTIVITY 1
Whole class, in threes

- *Recording tallies in a tally chart*

A dice, tally chart (PCM 45)

The children make two rows on their tally charts and write 'odd' and 'even' as headings. They throw the dice, recording with a tally mark whether the number shown by the dice is odd or even. Continue until one row has 20 tallies. How many has the other one? Give the tally chart a title. Repeat the activity for categories such as '1 to 3' and '4 to 6'.

ACTIVITY 2
2-3 children

- *Constructing a tally chart*

Different coloured interlocking cubes, tally chart – optional (PCM 45)

The children each take two handfuls of cubes and spread them out on the table. They then draw a tally chart to show how many cubes there are of each colour. (Some children may need to use the pre-drawn chart.) Give the tally chart a title.

ACTIVITY 3
3-4 children

- *Constructing and interpreting a tally chart*

Shape cards (sheets 1 and 2) (PCMs 42, 43), tally chart (PCM 45)

Spread the cards out on the table, face down. The children write the numbers 1 to 8 down the left column of the tally chart to represent the number of sides of the shapes. They take turns to reveal a card, count the number of sides of the shape, and draw a tally mark in the appropriate row of the chart. They continue until all the cards have been taken. They complete the tally chart by giving it a title and writing the totals. Discuss the results with them by looking at the tally chart.

ACTIVITY 4
2-4 children

- *Constructing and interpreting a tally chart*

A dice

The children write the dice numbers (1 to 6) in the left column of their tally chart. They take turns to throw the dice and make a tally mark to match the dice throw. The winner is the first to have two 'gates' (ten tallies) in any two rows of his chart. Finally, they construct a tally chart to represent their combined throws. Give each tally chart a title. Discuss the results with them.

D2 Frequency tables

ACTIVITY 1
Whole class, in threes

• *Constructing and interpreting a frequency table*
A dice, tally chart (PCM 45)
The children draw a blank frequency table headed 'Dice number' and 'Frequency'. Taking turns, they throw the dice 30 times and record each throw on the tally chart. After the thirtieth throw, they count how many of each number were thrown and record the results on the frequency table. Compare and discuss the tables. Construct a combined frequency table pooling the results of all the groups.

ACTIVITY 2
2-3 children

• *Constructing and interpreting a frequency table*
Playing cards (aces to tens)
The children draw a blank frequency table headed 'Suit' and 'Frequency'. They shuffle the cards and deal out 30, face up. They write 'hearts', 'clubs', 'diamonds' and 'spades' in the first column, then count how many of each suit they can see and complete the table. Repeat with a different 30 cards.

ACTIVITY 3
3-4 children

• *Constructing and interpreting a frequency table, sorting and naming shapes based on their number of sides*
A large collection of plastic 2-d shapes, a cloth bag
The children draw a blank frequency table headed 'Number of sides' and 'Frequency'. They place the shapes in the bag and draw them out, one at a time, grouping those which have the same number of sides. When all the shapes have been sorted, they complete the frequency table to show how many of each type there are. Finally, they write the correct name for each category, e.g. 'triangles', 'quadrilaterals'.

ACTIVITY 4
2-4 children

• *Constructing and interpreting a frequency table, comparing two frequency tables*
A page of text from a book
The children draw a blank frequency table headed 'Vowel' and 'Frequency', and write 'a', 'e', 'i', 'o' and 'u' in the first column. Looking at the page of text, they predict which vowel will appear most often and which least often. They then start with the letter 'a' and count how many times it appears on the page. They write the total against 'a' in the frequency column. They do the same for each of the other vowels. Discuss the results with them. Repeat with a different page of text and compare the results.

Bar graphs

ACTIVITY 1
Whole class, in pairs

• *Constructing a tally chart, drawing and interpreting a bar graph*
A book, blank bar graph (PCM 46), blank tally chart (PCM 45)
The children choose any page from the book and count the number of letters (3, 4, 5, 6, 7, 8, more than 8) in the first 50 words. They record the results in the tally chart, completing the totals. They then construct a bar graph based on the results of the tally chart. Discuss the results with them.

ACTIVITY 2
3-4 children

• *Constructing a tally chart, drawing and interpreting a bar graph*
A dice (numbered 3, 4, 5, 6, 7, 8), blank bar graph (PCM 46), blank tally chart (PCM 45)
The children take turns to throw the dice, recording each throw in the tally chart. They stop when one row has a total of ten throws, i.e. two 'gates'. They then draw a bar graph to show the results. Discuss with them what the bar graph shows.

ACTIVITY 3
4 children

• *Drawing and interpreting a bar graph*
Playing cards, blank bar graph (PCM 46)
Each child chooses a suit of cards. Shuffle the cards and spread out 30, face up. The children count their chosen suit of cards and draw a bar graph to show how many there are of each suit. Which suit appeared most? Which appeared least?

ACTIVITY 4
3-4 children

• *Using a computer to construct a bar graph*
Appropriate spreadsheet software or graphing program
The children use a simple graphing program or spreadsheet to create a bar graph for any of the above bar graph activities. They should discuss the display to ensure that the labelling is appropriate.

ACTIVITY 5
3-4 children

• *Constructing a tally chart, drawing and intepreting a bar graph*
Two dice, blank bar graph (PCM 46), blank tally chart (PCM 45)
The children investigate the results of rolling two dice and the total thrown. They decide on the number of throws, construct a tally chart and draw a corresponding bar graph to show the results. Discuss the results with them. Extend the activity by investigating the difference between the dice throws, i.e. 2 and 4, 3 and 3.

ACTIVITY 6
3-4 children

• *Collecting data, using a computer to construct a bar graph*
Spreadsheet software
The children conduct a simple survey recording their favourite fruits. Using the information gathered, they enter it into a spreadsheet, the fruits followed by the number of children who have chosen that fruit. The children then produce a bar graph and add the title and labels. A short word-processed report could then be written. Other information such as hair colours or birthdays could be similarly graphed.

ACTIVITY 1
Whole class, in pairs

• *Constructing and interpreting a pictograph in which one symbol represents two observations*

Different coloured interlocking cubes

Each child takes a handful of coloured cubes. They draw a pictograph to show how many of each colour they have collected. Choose a symbol, e.g. a square, to represent two cubes (half a square for one cube). Work out how many different colours of cubes they have, and write the colours down the vertical axis. Complete the graph and discuss the results with the children.

ACTIVITY 2
2-3 children

• *Constructing and interpreting pictographs in which one symbol represents both one observation and two observations*

A dice

The children draw a pictograph to show the results of throwing a dice 30 times. They decide on a symbol, e.g. a square, to represent one throw. They write the dice numbers down the vertical axis, throw the dice and fill in the graph. They discuss the final results. They then draw another pictograph to show the same results, but where the symbol represents two throws instead of one and half a symbol represents one throw.

ACTIVITY 3
3-4 children

• *Constructing and interpreting pictographs in which one symbol represents two observations*

A page of text

The children draw a pictograph to show how many of each vowel appear in the text. First they predict which vowel will appear most often, and which least. They write the five vowels down the vertical axis. They then decide on a symbol, e.g. a circle or square, to represent two appearances of the vowel. They complete the pictograph and discuss the results.

ACTIVITY 4
2-3 children

• *Constructing and interpreting pictographs in which one symbol represents four observations*

A list of children in the school

The children draw a pictograph to show how many children there are in each class in the school. They write the names of the classes down the vertical axis and decide on a symbol to represent four children. They must also decide how one, two and three children can be represented using parts of the symbol, so it is best to choose a symbol which can easily be divided into quarters, e.g. a circle or a square. They complete the pictograph and discuss the results.

0	1	2
3	4	5
6	7	8
9	10	

11	12	13
14	15	16
17	18	19
20		

21	**22**	**23**	**24**
25	**26**	**27**	**28**
29	**30**	**31**	**32**
33	**34**	**35**	**36**

37	38	39	40
41	42	43	44
45	46	47	48
49	50	51	52

53	54	55	56
57	58	59	60
<u>6</u><u>1</u>	62	63	64
65	<u>66</u>	67	<u>68</u>

6̲9̲	**70**	**71**	**72**
73	**74**	**75**	**76**
77	**78**	**79**	**80**
8̲1̲	**82**	**83**	**84**

85	<u>**86**</u>	**87**	**88**
<u>**89**</u>	**90**	<u>**91**</u>	**92**
93	**94**	**95**	**96**
97	<u>**98**</u>	<u>**99**</u>	**100**

50	100
40	90
30	80
20	70
10	60

45	95
35	85
25	75
15	65
5	55

1   0 0 5

2   0 0 4

3   0 0 3

4   0 0 2

5   0 0 1

6	0 0 0
7	0 0 8
8	0 0 7
9	0 0 9

1 0	
2 0	0 6
3 0	0 8
4 0	0 7
5 0	0 9

H (hundreds)	T (tens)	U (units)

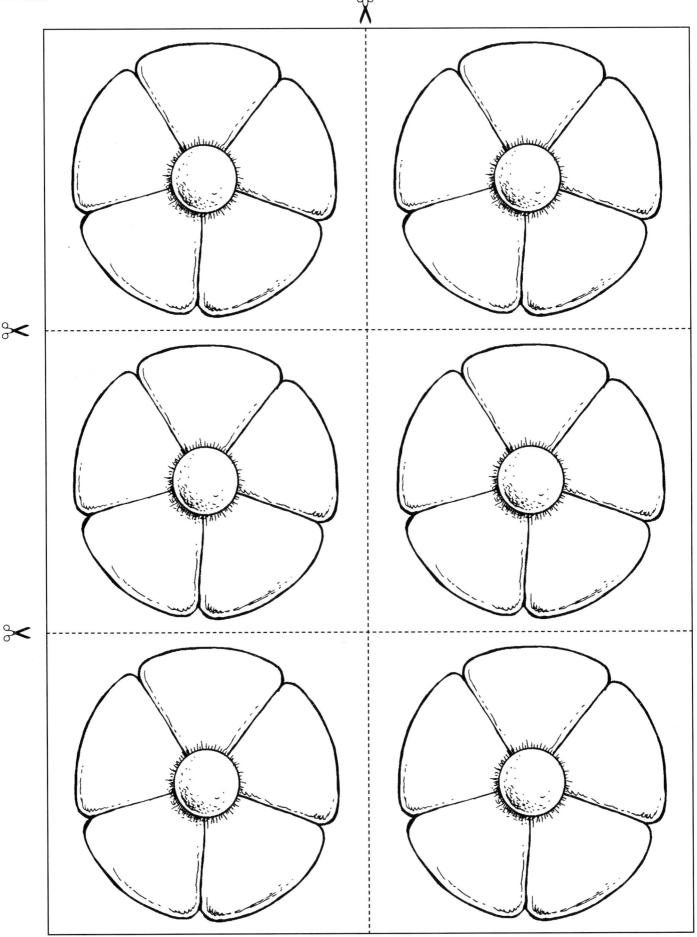

10	7	6	14
18	12	16	13
9	15	19	20
17	11	5	8

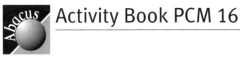

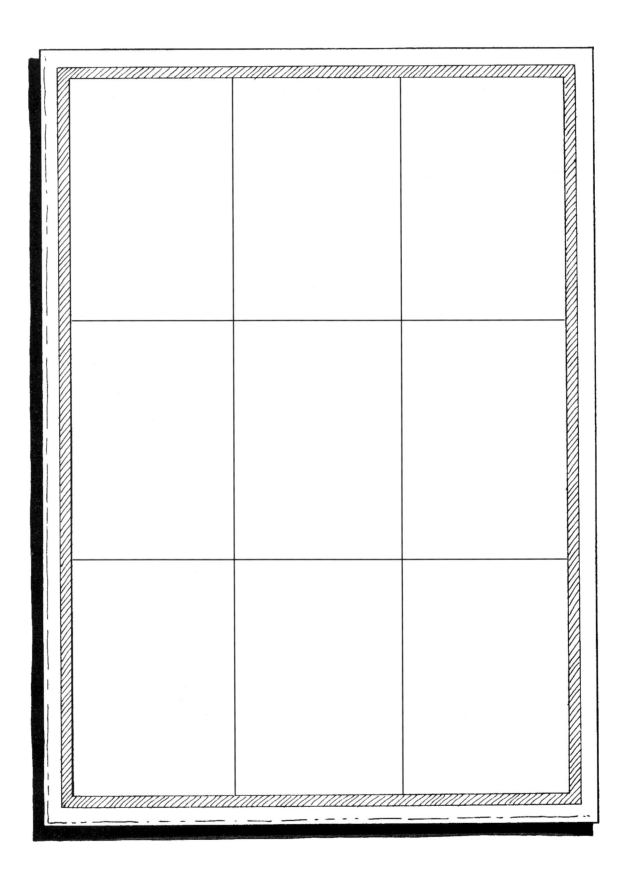

280	181	400	375	488
550	325	396	760	150
190	575	545	785	994
293	940	850	591	600
470	682	250	275	197

3	4	5	1	2
10	6	3	7	4
1	2	5	10	2
3	8	10	9	4
1	4	3	3	5

Cut out
this section

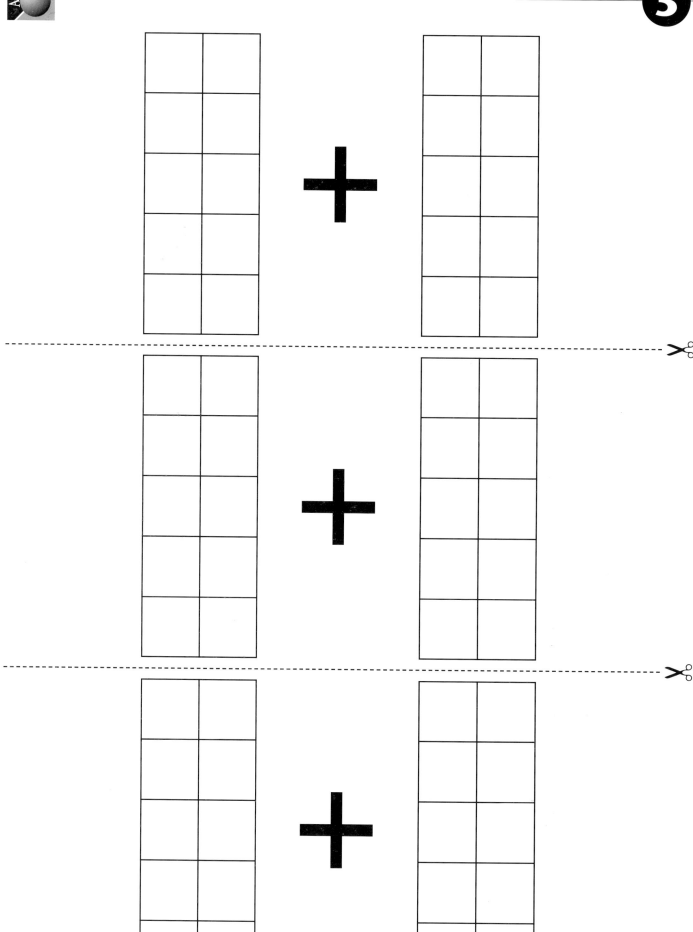

30p

29p

28p

27p

23p

24p

25p

26p

19p

20p

21p

22p

15p

16p

17p

18p

4×2	8×2	2×3	6×3
3×2	7×2	1×3	5×3
2×2	6×2	10×2	4×3
1×2	5×2	9×2	3×3

10×3	4×4	8×4	2×5
9×3	3×4	7×4	1×5
8×3	2×4	6×4	10×4
7×3	1×4	5×4	9×4

6×5	10×5	4×10	8×10
5×5	9×5	3×10	7×10
4×5	8×5	2×10	6×10
3×5	7×5	1×10	5×10

27 ÷ 3	15 ÷ 3	3 ÷ 3	28 ÷ 4
30 ÷ 3	18 ÷ 3	6 ÷ 3	32 ÷ 4
10 × 10	21 ÷ 3	9 ÷ 3	36 ÷ 4
9 × 10	24 ÷ 3	12 ÷ 3	40 ÷ 4

12 ÷ 4	18 ÷ 2	10 ÷ 2	2 ÷ 2
16 ÷ 4	20 ÷ 2	12 ÷ 2	4 ÷ 2
20 ÷ 4	4 ÷ 4	14 ÷ 2	6 ÷ 2
24 ÷ 4	8 ÷ 4	16 ÷ 2	8 ÷ 2

1 × 3 = 3	1 × 4 = 4
2 × 3 = 6	2 × 4 = 8
3 × 3 = 9	3 × 4 = 12
4 × 3 = 12	4 × 4 = 16
5 × 3 = 15	5 × 4 = 20
6 × 3 = 18	6 × 4 = 24
7 × 3 = 21	7 × 4 = 28
8 × 3 = 24	8 × 4 = 32
9 × 3 = 27	9 × 4 = 36
10 × 3 = 30	10 × 4 = 40

1 × 5 = 5	1 × 10 = 10
2 × 5 = 10	2 × 10 = 20
3 × 5 = 15	3 × 10 = 30
4 × 5 = 20	4 × 10 = 40
5 × 5 = 25	5 × 10 = 50
6 × 5 = 30	6 × 10 = 60
7 × 5 = 35	7 × 10 = 70
8 × 5 = 40	8 × 10 = 80
9 × 5 = 45	9 × 10 = 90
10 × 5 = 50	10 × 10 = 100

$$\frac{1}{2} \qquad \frac{1}{3} \qquad \frac{1}{4} \qquad \frac{1}{8}$$

$$\frac{1}{2} \qquad \frac{1}{3} \qquad \frac{1}{4} \qquad \frac{1}{8}$$

$\dfrac{1}{6}$	$\dfrac{2}{3}$	$\dfrac{2}{4}$	$\dfrac{3}{4}$
$\dfrac{1}{6}$	$\dfrac{2}{6}$	$\dfrac{3}{6}$	$\dfrac{4}{6}$
$\dfrac{5}{6}$	$\dfrac{2}{8}$	$\dfrac{3}{8}$	$\dfrac{4}{8}$
$\dfrac{5}{8}$	$\dfrac{6}{8}$	$\dfrac{7}{8}$	$\dfrac{2}{2}$

1	2	3	4	5	6	7	8	9	10
11	12	13	14	15	16	17	18	19	20
21	22	23	24	25	26	27	28	29	30
31	32	33	34	35	36	37	38	39	40
41	42	43	44	45	46	47	48	49	50
51	52	53	54	55	56	57	58	59	60
61	62	63	64	65	66	67	68	69	70
71	72	73	74	75	76	77	78	79	80
81	82	83	84	85	86	87	88	89	90
91	92	93	94	95	96	97	98	99	100

0	1	2	3	4	5	6	7	8	9
10	11	12	13	14	15	16	17	18	19
20	21	22	23	24	25	26	27	28	29
30	31	32	33	34	35	36	37	38	39
40	41	42	43	44	45	46	47	48	49
50	51	52	53	54	55	56	57	58	59
60	61	62	63	64	65	66	67	68	69
70	71	72	73	74	75	76	77	78	79
80	81	82	83	84	85	86	87	88	89
90	91	92	93	94	95	96	97	98	99

Blank fraction lines $\left(\frac{1}{3}, \frac{1}{4}, \frac{1}{6}, \frac{1}{8}, \frac{1}{10}\right)$

3

clockwise **1 right angle**	**clockwise** **2 right angles**
clockwise **3 right angles**	**clockwise** **4 right angles**
anticlockwise **1 right angle**	**anticlockwise** **2 right angles**
anticlockwise **3 right angles**	**anticlockwise** **4 right angles**

West	West	West
South	South	South
East	East	East
North	North	North

4:40	**10:06**	**12:05**
8:07	**2:15**	**5:20**
7:35	**9:40**	**11:30**
6:32	**4:25**	**3:55**
12:50	**1:24**	**6:10**

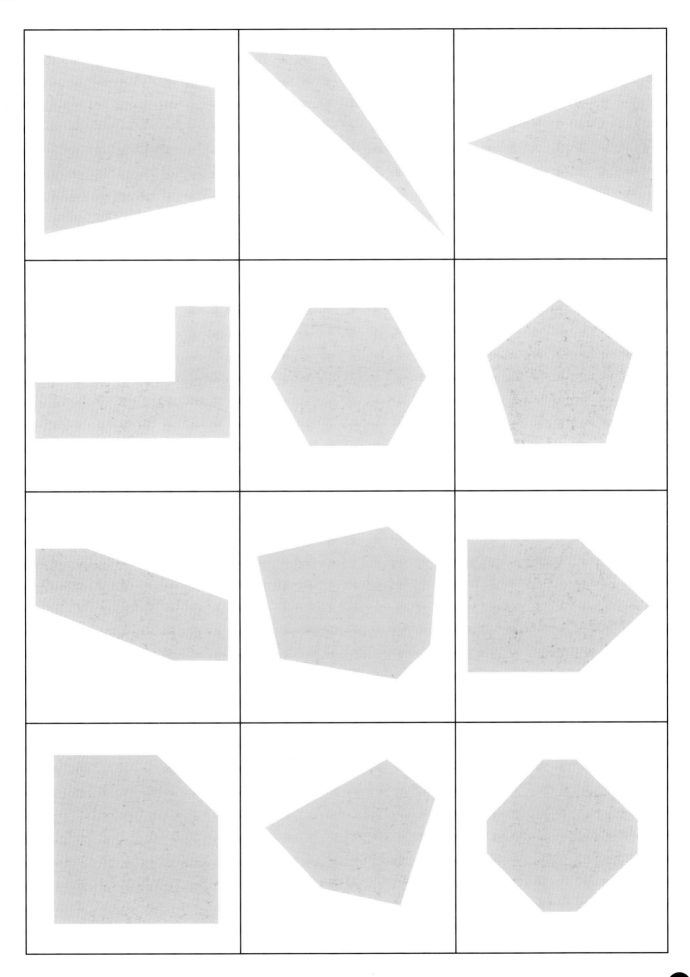

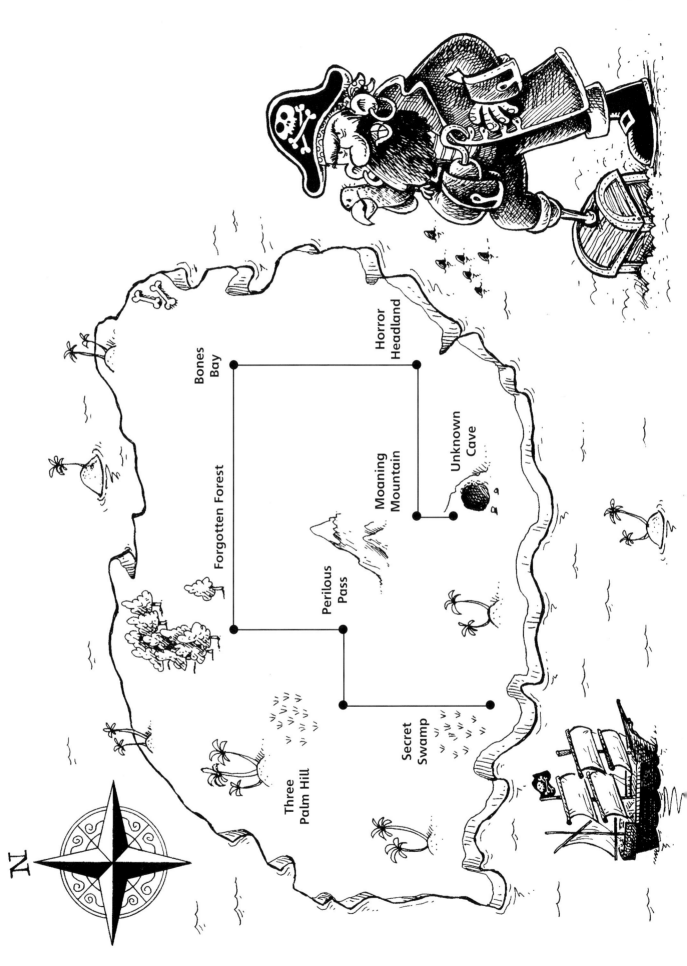

Title: _____

	Tallies	Total

Title: _____

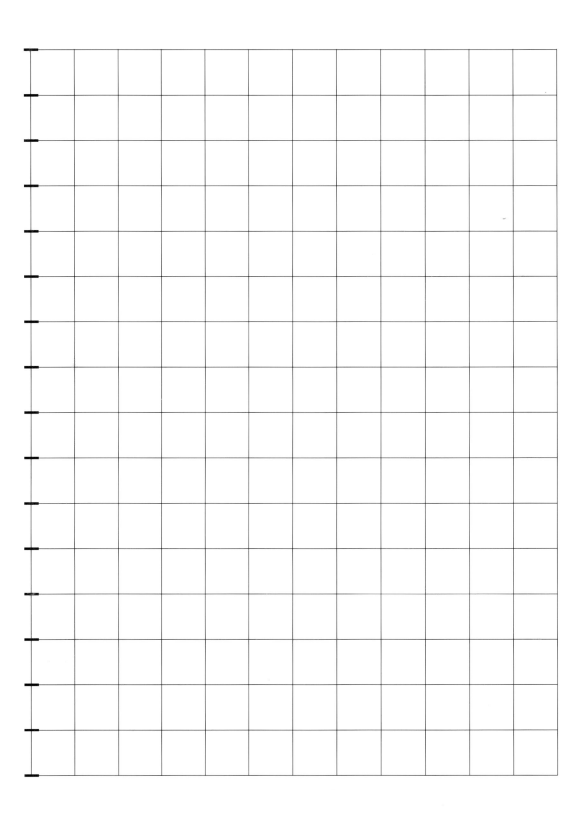